IS IT TRUE WHAT THEY SAY ABOUT FLYING?

Airlines say you're safe as in your living room. Critics call every flight a gamble. And millions of passengers have only that sinking feeling as their guide.

Pulling no punches, bestselling author Robert J. Serling sets the record straight. Here is the full story behind the airline's official safety record, and detailed reconstructions of the crashes that have marred it. The latest technological advances, and their accompanying dangers. The revealing case history of the controversial Electra jetliner. The current quality of airline personnel. The problem of the air traffic "crush." And everything else you need and want to know before you strap on your safety belt with confidence.

W9-CIO-701

LOUD
AND
CLEAR

Robert J. Serling

COMPLETELY REVISED EDITION

A DELL BOOK

Published by
Dell Publishing Co., Inc.
750 Third Avenue
New York, New York 10017
Reprinted by arrangement with Doubleday & Company, Inc.,
New York, New York
Dell ® TM 681510, Dell Publishing Co., Inc.

Printed in the United States of America
First printing—June 1970
Second printing—August 1970
Third printing—November 1970

CONTENTS

INTRODUCTION TO THE DELL EDITION ... 1

1. "One Eighth of an Iceberg . . ." ... 3
2. The First Ten Years ... 39
3. "It's What's Up Front That Counts" ... 59
4. "They Bought the Farm . . ." ... 111
5. The Electra Story ... 184
6. The 727—The Libeled Airplane ... 251
7. How Do You Walk Away? ... 284
8. Fire Away ... 330
9. ". . . Skipper's Shot!" ... 356
10. Collision Course ... 382
11. The Critics ... 427
12. The Yonder in the Wild Blue ... 460

POSTSCRIPT ... 486
NOTES ... 490

Introduction to the Dell Edition

You are about to read what might be termed a positive book about a negative subject.

Namely, air safety.

No one can treat this topic objectively unless he writes about the bad as well as the good. Therefore it was inevitable that in telling the story of the first ten years of the jet age, I had to recount some of the tragedies along with the triumphs. Some may be frightened and disturbed by such accounts. They should not be, if they take the simple precaution of not reading out of context.

This book is neither a hatchet job nor a whitewash effort. It is an honest effort to tell the truth about air travel —past, present, and future. When it was first published by Doubleday as a hardback, a few critics labeled me a mouthpiece for the airlines while a few other critics suggested that the airlines have me deported for scaring people. I hope that these wide-apart poles of judgment are evidence of a work that is smack down the middle.

The Dell edition represents thousands of additional words, considerable revision, and voluminous updating of the original work. It also corrects, I trust, all or at least most of the inadvertent errors that crept into the original edition. It also happens to be one chapter longer than the Doubleday hardback, a chapter that condenses an earlier work—*The Electra Story* (also Doubleday, 1963)—which is now out of print. I still receive requests for the Electra book and Doubleday was kind enough to grant permission to include the Electra mystery in this Dell edition.

Furthermore, although the Electra was not really a part

of the jet age story, its history offered proof of what government-industry cooperation can accomplish in a crisis involving air safety.

In order to make this edition as up-to-date as possible, I have added at press time a series of notes, identified in the text by a figure in parentheses.

ROBERT J. SERLING

1. "ONE EIGHTH OF
AN ICEBERG . . ."

One day in May 1967, five men boarded a gleaming new jetliner freshly hatched out of Boeing's massive factory in Renton, Washington.

The plane was a three-engine 727, affectionately dubbed the "three-holer" by crews flying the tri-jet. This one bore the red, white, and blue markings of Northwest Orient Airlines, with NWA's traditional scarlet tail, but for the job it was to do on this warm spring day it could have been any one of the nine hundred and eighty-seven Boeing jets delivered to the world's airlines up to this date.

This particular aircraft was N499US, ship number 499 being the last of Northwest's original order of thirty 727s. It was about to engage in what the industry terms an acceptance flight, a series of searching inspections plus ground and flight operational tests conducted by personnel of the purchasing airline. It is a thorough, sometimes brutal examination of an airliner. If an automobile buyer put a new car through inspections and tests equivalent to an acceptance flight, the process would consume at least two full days, not counting time for any necessary corrective work.

You are going along on this acceptance flight. It is an airline operation that the flying public is never privileged to observe; for that matter, only a handful of pilots have engaged in such flights. Most airlines use test crews especially trained for the job, since it calls for many operations quite different from those familiar to line pilots.

Your companions today are a special test crew. All three flight crew members, with many years' experience as

3

regular line pilots, are well acquainted with a line crew's needs and viewpoints, a fact which fits neatly with the peculiar demands of test work. In charge of the acceptance flight is Captain Paul Soderlind, whose official title lists him as Northwest's Director of Flight Operations—Technical. He ranks among the world's finest pilots. A tall, soft-spoken, balding man, he was awarded the coveted Air Line Pilots Association's Annual Air Safety Award plus a Flight Safety Foundation award and a medal from the FAA "for extraordinary service," all for his flight tests, studies, lectures, and other work involving the operation of jet airplanes in severe turbulence.

The copilot is a younger man, Dean Sunde. He is slim, dark, and handsome, and has a wry, rather puckish sense of humor. The flight engineer, like Sunde a permanent member of Soderlind's division, is Glen Doan, who also is a qualified pilot. He is older than Sunde, outwardly more serious, and shares with the copilot an obvious respect and affection for Soderlind.

You are breakfasting with your crew at 7 A.M. in a motel close to Seattle-Tacoma International Airport. A waitress has put down the coffee when two men join the group. Soderlind introduces them. The first is Len Larson, Northwest's Superintendent of Engineering Services, who will be handling the voluminous paperwork that must transpire between NWA and Boeing before the 727 is turned over to the airline (it was said by some wag that the weight of the paperwork must equal the weight of the airplane before the transfer can be consummated).

"He's very, very important," Soderlind chuckles. "He's got the check."

The second arrival is George Dalin, Northwest's Superintendent of Quality Control. Dalin (Soderlind calls him "our advance man") arrived in Seattle a day early and spent all of that day inspecting the exterior and interior of the airplane. He checks everything from the quality of the airplane's construction to the operation of the coffee makers. A scratch on a window, for example, would send Dalin straight to a Boeing man with a quiet but firm request for immediate replacement.

"She's pretty clean," he advises Soderlind. "A few minor items but they've all been taken care of. They're still installing one of the galleys but should be finished by the time we get to the airplane."

Soderlind explains that Northwest used to—and most airlines still do—conduct an acceptance flight with a Boeing test crew in Seattle before formally accepting a plane. But Boeing's Production Test flight crews and their line maintenance men do such a good job of presenting "clean" airplanes to the customer, Northwest is satisfied with a "fly-away" acceptance. Under an agreement with Boeing, NWA formally accepts and pays for the airplane before the acceptance flight test. Its crew then conducts all of the test items during the delivery flight to NWA's home base at Minneapolis-St. Paul. This procedure has advantages for both companies. It releases a Boeing test crew for other duty, it makes good use of the otherwise unproductive but necessary ferry flight time to Minneapolis-St. Paul, and it gets the airplane into scheduled service one day earlier. And with the tremendous productivity of a jetliner, the importance of that extra day's availability cannot be underestimated. A 727 can gross about $25,000 every working day.

"Is this the first time the plane has been flown?" you ask.

"No," Soderlind answers. "Sandy MacMurray's boys—Sandy is Boeing's Chief of Production Flight Test—they'll have flown it anywhere from one to five times to get it ready for us. How many flights has 499 had, Len?"

"Three. And all squawks cleaned up, they tell me."

Soderlind nods approvingly.

"Boeing is as anxious as we are for a perfect delivery," he explains. "And Sandy's flight crews really know how to go over an airplane. Maybe you didn't know this, but Boeing puts a warranty on a new jet just as an automobile manufacturer does on a car. The basic warranty is for two years or the first five thousand hours of flight, whichever comes first, plus an airframe service life policy for thirty thousand hours. That can amount to nearly a lifetime as far as the airplane's usefulness to the airline is concerned. Then there are the individual warranties of the vendors —the subcontractors who supply the various components. These are usually good for two years."

"Boeing pays for the acceptance-ferry flight," Larson adds, "and for fixing whatever squawks we find on our test flight, even after we give them the final dough."

You wonder out loud what the flight will cost Boeing.

"About seven hundred bucks," Larson says. "That's

5

mostly for fuel. Northwest pays our salaries, of course. Want to see the check we'll give them?"

He takes an envelope out of his pocket and hands it over. Your eyes focus on the amount. Three million, five hundred and one thousand, two hundred and fifty-six dollars and fifty cents. The attached stub carried this information:

> In payment of balance due on delivery of Boeing model 727-51C aircraft No. N499US serial number 19290, being the last of four Block G aircraft under purchase agreement No. 86. Base price $4,996,-795.00. Add change orders 10-15 $3500. Less advance payment of $1,499,038.50

"What are change orders?" you ask.

"Special modifications Northwest requires," Larson replies. "For example, as I remember, that thirty-five hundred bucks was for relocating the flight recorder to the rear of the fuselage, a more 'crash-worthy' location. Incidentally, that five-million-dollar price tag doesn't include the seats or the galleys, or a lot of the electronics equipment. There's about one hundred fifty thousand dollars worth of radio and navigation gear that comes extra. One galley runs about twenty-five thousand dollars and the ninety-three seats cost another sixty-five thousand."

Soderlind interrupts. "Time to get to work. You got a car, Len?"

"Yes, sir. I'm ready whenever you guys are."

The ride to Boeing's Commercial Delivery Center at Boeing Field takes only fifteen minutes. It is a Saturday and the Delivery Center looks less hectic than on a weekday. Larson drives up to the gate guarding the Delivery Center where Boeing's flight test crews conduct their production test flights and the line crews work off any squawks that are found. The Northwest men show their identification badges and the thought strikes you that for what is in the envelope Larson is carrying, the guard could have been a bit more enthusiastic in his welcome.

You walk into the Delivery Center building and through clean but rather Spartan corridors, glancing at the signs hanging over the entrances to various small offices. Soderlind tells you the rooms are used by Boeing customers, many of whom maintain permanent representatives at the

Center. The signs are an airline roll call: *TWA* . . .
UNITED . . . *AIR FRANCE* . . . *AMERICAN* . . .

Finally you come to the Northwest office. Its most prominent item of furniture is a big desk on which Soderlind places a large red loose-leaf book marked "727 SHIP MANUAL," plus a small mountain of what appear to be other engineering and operations manuals.

"You guys can go on out to the airplane and start the ground checks while I talk to Seattle Dispatch and work out a flight plan," Soderlind says to his crew.

Larson, Sunde, Doan, and Dalin leave. Soderlind pulls a pad of forms out of his flight bag and begins working out the flight plan. He is planning to fly Jet 90 to Billings, Jet 32 to Aberdeen and Jet 34 (these are the jet routes he will use) on into Minneapolis-St. Paul. He uses a navigational computer—a circular slide rule—that is as much a part of a pilot as his uniform. First he checks with NWA's Seattle Dispatch office and gets a complete briefing on the weather, airport conditions, and all the other factors that must be considered. He figures on a fuel load of 23,700 pounds for the en route portion of the flight, at his desired altitude of 33,000 feet where the temperature will be 58° F below zero. He adds another 9,000 pounds of fuel for the one hour of special test flying that will be required. To this Soderlind tacks on the fuel that will be needed if it becomes necessary to proceed to an alternate airport, and, of course, enough reserve fuel for a minimum of forty-five minutes.

This painstaking computing of the fuel load is a little academic, Soderlind admits, because on the acceptance flight the crew merely wants all tanks full—50,000 pounds in round numbers—so they can more closely duplicate the weight and performance of a scheduled flight. He goes on to explain:

"About one hour's worth of the required testing—things like compass checks, stick shaker checks, gear, and flap operating time checks, and others—can't be done during the en route portion of the flight, so we'll take time out in the Billings, Montana, area for the 'local' work. We normally do this at Billings for a number of good reasons. The weather there is usually good and the traffic is light. The fact that I was born and raised there has absolutely nothing to do with it."

A Boeing employee sticks his head in the door and announces, "She's all cleaned up and ready to go, Captain Soderlind."

Soderlind smiles and phones Seattle Dispatch with his flight plan—a conglomeration of meaningless hieroglyphics to your layman's eyes, but which in reality is a carefully computed blueprint that predicts times between checkpoints and fuel to be used, based on such factors as altitude, winds, temperatures, gross weight, and planned true airspeed.

"We can go out to the airplane now," he says, "but first you have to sign this little piece of paper."

The "little piece of paper" turns out to be a waiver of all claims against Northwest if anything goes wrong. Its wording is very much to the point and slightly disconcerting.

> In consideration of his participation in a flight of a model 727-51C, N499US, aircraft operated by Northwest Airlines, Inc., on May 27, 1967, the undersigned agrees to assume all risk of accident and loss of every character including personal injury, death and loss or damage to property, and agrees that Northwest Airlines, Inc., shall not be liable for any loss, damage, injury or death whether caused by the negligence of Northwest Airlines, Inc., or its agents or otherwise, which arises out of or is in any way connected with such flight.

You sign it, handing the paper to Soderlind with a wistful "Kindly refrain from negligence, Captain."

"Don't worry," he grins. "Many of the things we'll be doing on this flight will be a little different from a regular scheduled flight, but we won't scare you too much. Every gizmo on the airplane will be checked in all its normal and emergency functions before we'll let the machine carry any passengers. Let's go."

You enter the 727 through its rear belly stairs, noting as you walk through the cavernous, empty cabin that all the seats are covered with plastic jackets. Dalin and Larson are still checking various pieces of cabin equipment while simultaneously keeping their eyes on the Boeing workmen finishing up the installation of the galley.

"Everything's fine," Dalin tells Soderlind, "including the coffee maker."

With that slip of paper you recently signed fresh in mind, you cannot help asking if the checked-out items include the inflatable emergency chutes.

"You don't need to worry," Soderlind assures you. "Every item on the airplane, including the operation of the toilet flush buttons, has been gone over."

You enter the cockpit while Soderlind stows his "brainbag"—the flight kit that every pilot carries to hold the manuals, computers, and other tools of his trade.

"I love the 727," he remarks, "but its cockpit isn't the biggest in the world when it comes to room for flight kits."

Sunde already is sitting in the right seat, armed with a twenty-page document, the top of which carries the simple title "NWA Acceptance Test—Boeing 727-51." He is down to the eighteenth item on the 227-item list that starts out with such prosaic equipment as rudder pedal adjustment, instrument panel fasteners, and the cockpit seats themselves.

"How far have you got?" Soderlind inquires, taking out a duplicate document.

"Eighteen—fire warning lights, bell cutouts, and 'shutoff' items."

"Everything okay so far?"

"You bet. Everything good down to where we are so far."

"How about the seat placards?" Soderlind asks with a slight grin.

"Thought our visitor might like to check that out."

"Better follow him through," Soderlind says. "Most important item in the cockpit. Look down at the back of my seat and read me that red placard."

You comply, doing a double-take at the message. "SEAT MUST FACE FORWARD DURING TAKEOFF AND LANDING."

"Do they figure you might want to face sideways on takeoff or landing?" you ask incredulously.

Soderlind laughs. "Must be. That placard's on every Boeing pilot seat I've ever seen. I've never taken the trouble to find out why."

(You find out later that the sign refers to the jump or observer's seat in back of the captain's and is located so as to be seen by the occupant of the jump seat. On most 727s, this seat is movable on tracks sideways and rotates through a 360-degree arc.)

Doan announces that he's going outside for a walk-around inspection, and hoists himself out of the flight engineer's seat. Soderlind and Sunde resume work on the 47 cockpit items that still must be functionally checked before the engines are started.

Fire-switch operation of fuel valves, hydraulic pump lights and generator breakers . . . thrust levers . . . flight recorder . . . overspeed warning . . . stick shaker . . . Pilot-static heat . . . parking brakes and light . . . flaps and slats, positions 0°, 2°, 5°, 15°, 25°, 30° and 40° and annunciator lights . . .

Every system that can be functionally checked on the ground is checked there, not only to ensure its proper operation, but because the checks can be run on the ground without worrying about other traffic on actual flying of the airplane. Although nearly everything will be rechecked in flight, the ground work means the flight checks can be accomplished more quickly and with less diversion of attention.

One thing that impresses you as Soderlind's crew conducts the ground checks is the voluminous backup equipment in almost every area—a redundant, duplicate system for use if a primary component goes haywire. Hydraulic and pneumatic brake pressures must be within certain limits. Flaps and slats must extend and retract in a specific number of seconds using the normal hydraulic system, and in a longer but nevertheless just as specific time using the alternate electric flap operation system.

When all of the jet's systems have been functionally inspected, the three engines are started. Now Soderlind and his two colleagues are going over engine instrumentation *. . . engine pressure ratio* (the crew calls it "Eeper") *. . . low compressor RPM . . . high compressor RPM . . . exhaust gas temperature . . . fuel flow . . . oil pressure . . . oil temperature . . . pneumatic pressure . . . engine vibration level . . .*

All this is checked both with the engines idling and at takeoff thrust. Every reading is carefully recorded. Such abstract-sounding things as N1-for-surge-bleed-valve operation, wing anti-ice overheat warning, reverse thrust temperature detent values—it is all Greek to you but each is carefully scrutinized and recorded. Finally the engines are each accelerated from idle RPM to takeoff RPM with a "thrust lever burst."

"They must accelerate from idle to takeoff thrust in not

more than eight seconds and there can't be more than one-second difference among the three engines," Soderlind says.

On 499, as the fuel flow and temperature gauges move rapidly in their tiny, instrument-encased orbits, all three engines reach takeoff thrust in just over six seconds and Soderlind nods happily. The final preflight check is to pressurize the cabin partially and check the "air data" instruments to see that there are no leaks in the static system lines to the airspeed indicators, the altimeters, and other important flight instruments. There are none. Soderlind's list thus far is a long series of checks by the word SATISFACTORY and there are none by the word UNSATISFACTORY.

"Let's go get a cup of coffee and tell Len he can buy it," Soderlind announces.

The paperwork involving the official transfer of N499US from the Boeing Company to Northwest Airlines, Inc., takes about thirty minutes—the final act being the handing over of the keys to the cockpit door. You walk back to the plane and sit in the cockpit jump seat behind the two pilots.

Takeoff.

From the world of the flight deck it is a thrilling yet simultaneously routine procedure. Exciting in a visual sense, for the view from the flight deck is something a passenger never sees—the 727 gulping down the long ribbon of concrete and the quiet but firm voice of the copilot as he calls out the significant airspeeds.

". . . V_1" (the maximum speed at which the takeoff can be aborted) . . .

". . . ROTATE!" (when the pilot begins to lift the nose so the airplane will lift off the ground) . . .

Soderlind pulls back gently on the column, and the nose comes up about 16 degrees. The 727 climbs effortlessly, as if there were a giant pushing at her with a huge hand under her belly.

During the climb to 33,000, more functional checks are completed. Climb trim, control centering, the "barber pole" position (the Mach/airspeed warning band), autopilot coupling to the VOR (Very high frequency Omnidirectional Radio Range) course, captain and copilot airspeed indicator agreement, engine performance, thrust lever trim and a host of other things.

About thirty minutes after takeoff, Soderlind asks Sunde

11

to request a clearance from Air Traffic Control for an approach and landing at Missoula, Montana. When the clearance comes through Soderlind reduces engine thrust to idle and begins the descent from cruise altitude. And now begins a special phase of the flight, not related to the acceptance testing.

"Northwest serves what we call the mountain stations," Soderlind explains. "Missoula, Helena, Butte, and Bozeman, all in the mountains of Montana. These airports all present operating problems considerably different from our other stations, primarily because they're closely and almost completely surrounded by or are very near rugged mountainous terrain. Not only that, the four stations are an average of only about sixty-five miles apart, or about fifteen minutes as the jet flies. This means that a large portion of the flight is used in climb and descent maneuvering and this, in mountainous terrain, calls for somewhat different procedures. Several months ago, we flew a 727 into all of these stations to get a better feel for the peculiar problems involved. So on this trip, Ben Griggs [Vice President of Flight Operations and Soderlind's boss] asked that we take another look at the Missoula and Butte operations. That's what we're starting now."

At Missoula, Soderlind flies a simulated ILS (Instrument Landing System) approach to Runway 11. There actually is no ILS at Missoula, but one is simulated for the purposes of this flight by flying a pre-computed profile of altitude vs DME (Distance Measuring Equipment) miles from the Missoula VOR/DME station on the airport. The approach is down the valley that extends northwest of the airport, in clear weather, and Soderlind and crew carefully evaluate clearance from the mountains on both sides of the flight path.

"Looks good, boss," Sunde says. "I think an ILS on Runway 11 would work out fine."

Soderlind makes a touch-and-go landing and on the pullout reduces the thrust on the center engine to idle. The 727 doesn't even breathe a little bit harder.

"It's a good test," Soderlind explains as he climbs to cruise altitude and heads toward Butte. "The center engine is the most critical to lose since there's more drag than if either pod engine were inoperative."

The approach to Butte is even more interesting because the airport has high mountains close in on all sides.

"As one of our boys put it," Soderlind chuckles, "the best way into Butte is on a stepladder."

There is no control tower at Butte but Sunde calls the FAA's Flight Service Station for traffic and field condition advisories. Although it's not as bad as it looks, you are sure the right wing tip is brushing the trees as Soderlind circles for a landing on Runway 33. The captain points out that the maneuvering area is limited, which is the precise reason for these careful survey flights.

The landing is rough and Soderlind grins ruefully while Sunde murmurs disrespectfully, "Tell me when we're on."

Although the runway is about 6,800 feet long, Butte's high altitude, in effect, shortens that length. The thin air at this more-than-a-mile-above-sea-level airport makes for higher than normal landing speeds.

"With this factor, and a slight downhill slope the way we landed, you don't worry about greasing it on," Soderlind remarks in a half apology. "Getting it on the ground before using up much runway is a hell of a lot more important than a smooth touchdown. You can't stop these things in the air."

When ready for takeoff, Soderlind takes a minute to explain to the FAA man in the Flight Service Station that he'll be throttling an engine on takeoff for test purposes. There is a discreet silence for a moment before the FSS attendant answers, "I'm glad you're doing it and not me."

You worry aloud about this deliberate throttling of an engine on takeoff.

"Don't worry," the captain says. "We don't go around risking a five-million-dollar airplane. Or our own skins either. We know the performance of this machine down to a gnat's eyebrow, and we don't operate from runways where, if an engine failed at the worst point, we couldn't either stop or continue the climb-out with adequate obstruction clearance. You might be interested to know that every tree, house, pole, and every other kind of obstruction is plotted in the area off the runway edge, and the performance computations take every one into account. Sure, in the thin air of a mountain station like Butte, the airplane isn't going to perform like it does at sea level. But it's a simple matter of adjusting the weight to the runway length, elevation, and other factors. In other words, we reduce the load to the point where our engine-out performance is still adequate."

"When we reach V_1," Soderlind tells Sunde, "throttle number two to idle."

The 727 starts rolling, its turbines howling like a thousand panthers. Doan, the flight engineer, is eying the engine instruments like a hungry hawk so he can immediately warn Captain Soderlind of any trouble.

"V_1," Sunde calls, and in one motion pulls the number two thrust lever to idle.

"ROTATE!" Soderlind pulls the nose up for the lift-off.

You look down those 6,800 feet of asphalt, a little over a mile long but a rectangularly shaped postage stamp to your layman's eyes—particularly with a foreboding mountain directly ahead, its shrub-spotted bulk squatting peacefully under the warm sun.

Your heart beats a little faster. The 727 shoves her snout into the air and breaks ground, clawing her way over the mountain ahead with impertinent ease.

"Quite a machine," Soderlind murmurs. You have the feeling he would enjoy getting out and patting the 727 affectionately on her metal hide.

The throttled engine is left at idle until cruise altitude is reached, to simulate completely the situation where a scheduled flight might lose an engine on takeoff and have to continue to Billings or somewhere else.

"Does that last takeoff mean you can operate the 727 into Butte?" you ask.

"Not until more work is done on improving airport approach aids and other facilities," Soderlind replies. "There's no question about the 727's performance abilities as far as the mountain stations are concerned, but special procedures will have to be developed, too. You look a little green around the gills. Were you scared?"

"A little," you confess. "That damned runway looked about as long as the sidewalk in front of my house."

"There really wasn't anything to worry about," he assures you (slightly too late). "We know what this machine will do under just about any set of conditions. Well, let's head over toward Billings and start the local test work."

This phase of the acceptance flight is started about 75 miles west of Billings, and the first item is the stick shaker checks. These involve the simple process of reducing thrust and holding the nose up until the airflow over the wings reduces to near the point where all lift is lost. The stick shaker is a stall warning device and Soderlind wants to de-

14

termine the accuracy of the system that warns the pilot when lift margins are getting too low. The checks are done with the flaps at different positions, and the airspeed at which the stick shaker operates is compared carefully with the proper "book" figures. It's an interesting experience, to say the least, and again something no passenger will ever encounter because a qualified airline pilot is not going to let his lift margins get too low. But if it happened, the stick shaker would provide plenty of warning. It lets a pilot feel a stall developing on his controls before a stall actually occurs.

Soderlind makes three stall warning checks. The first is with the flaps set at zero or in the cruise configuration. The warning according to the book is supposed to occur at 150 knots at our particular weight. The nose comes up and the airspeed drops off gradually. There is a rattling sound when the stick shaker actuates, so called because it really shakes the control column. The 727 trembles in the buffeting of a near-stall, as if shaking her body in protest. Soderlind recovers by lowering the nose, extending partial flaps and applying near-takeoff thrust.

"The shaker sounded at one-five-three," Soderlind reports. "Three knots above the book, but actually right on the nose. The difference is due to our altitude. Now we check it with fifteen-degree flaps."

This time 499's shaker comes on at 119 knots, just one knot above the book value. With 40-degree flap the shaker is heard at 98, again within one knot of the book number. Soderlind is eminently satisfied and goes on to other tests, such as turning off all the control boost switches to see how the 727 responds without its "power steering."

Next the flaps and landing gear are each operated with their emergency backup systems. Lowering the landing gear with the emergency system calls for inserting a crank in three separate holes in the floor—one for each gear— and cranking a specific number of turns in a specific pattern. It takes a lot longer than the normal gear extension, which Soderlind has already tested and timed.

Soderlind tucks the snout of the 727 down to a lower altitude and the brown and green terrain of Montana flashes under the swept-back wings. Directly ahead is a small town and the altimeter is unwinding steadily until it reads only 5,500 above sea level.

"That's Rapelje coming up," Soderlind tells you. "I was

raised there from the time I was one year old until we moved to Columbus when I was eleven, and then to Billings a year later. Went to school in that brick building right in the center of town. Kinda like to come over the old town whenever I get the chance. It's so small, the city limits signs for both ends of town are on the same post. It's not only small, it's dry. I remember one year after a long dry spell, a drop of rain hit one of the farmers on the south side of town and he fainted. Took two buckets of sand to bring him to again."

Rapelje apparently is taking Soderlind's nostalgic visit with admirable calm. You don't see any citizens looking up at the 727 as it screams over the few buildings. You wonder what's going through the mind of this calm, so quietly efficient airline captain. Remembering his boyhood? His dreams of becoming a pilot? His early years in a farm community so tiny and peaceful that the 727 almost seems to have flown back in time, an unwelcome intruder showing off its technological muscles to a world that couldn't care less?

By now 499 is ten miles past Rapelje and Soderlind eases up the nose to climb back to 37,000 for the remainder of the flight to Minneapolis-St. Paul.

During the climb the crew goes through a fuel-dumping procedure, ejecting between 60 and 75 gallons from various tanks and drawing from Doan the wry comment that "we oughta send the bill to local mosquito control."

At 37,000 feet Soderlind checks engine acceleration and surge characteristics by rapid thrust lever cuts, one engine at a time to check for proper restart capability.

Everything works fine but Soderlind recalls with amusement the time they were running engine shut-down checks on a new Boeing 707.

"We got a call from an American flight just behind us," he laughs. "He tells us, 'Northwest, do you know you've got a slight pucker in your left contrail?' "

As you start the descent from 37,000 feet in preparation for landing at Minneapolis-St. Paul, you note that Soderlind pulls the thrust levers all the way to idle. You ask how this multi-ton monster is going to stay in the air.

"Most jet descents from cruise altitude," he explains, "are made with the engines at or near idle thrust. Although the engines produce a small amount of thrust even at idle, for all practical purposes the airplane is gliding.

16

The 727 is so aerodynamically clean—we call it 'slippery' —that from this altitude it will glide nearly a hundred and thirty miles. Far more, incidentally, than the smallest and lightest of private airplanes. Not only that, it does it at an average of about three hundred and eighty knots, or four hundred thirty-five miles per hour."

The final few remaining tests are completed during the approach and landing. You taxi in to Northwest's main base, a complex of windowless hangars, offices, parking lots, shops, and storerooms that cover some seventy-six acres. Soderlind, Sunde and Doan hold a conference over the voluminous notes they have made during the flight. The attitude indicator on the captain's side has been intermittently sticky. A generator frequency meter is inoperative. One radio headset is faulty, and Sunde has written up an item on "poor audio quality when using first officer's mike." The weather radar acted up about thirty minutes out and Soderlind has also entered a squawk about the squelch on a communications receiver, plus "loop rotator switch on right ADF [Automatic Direction Finder] sticks."

"Not bad," Soderlind says. "When you consider putting together thousands upon thousands of parts, it's truly amazing that we find so few items. It always takes several regular trips before any new airplane is 'squawk-free.' And, of course, we're literally a fault-finding crew—that's our function—so we expect to find things to complain about even on a plane that's just about perfect. Yep, our mechanics will have a few hours' work before 499 goes into service, but she'll be carrying passengers by tomorrow morning."

You deplane through the rear belly stairs, half hoping in your inevitable Walter Mitty mood that the mechanics may figure you were one of the test crew. The mechanics couldn't care less if you were Charles Lindbergh climbing off their airplane. They're concerned only with the squawks in the logbook that Soderlind hands them. As Paul Soderlind said, 499 has to be carrying passengers the next morning—swiftly, efficiently, comfortably, and safely.

You accompany him to his office in Northwest's general offices adjoining the hangars. Your eyes fall on a cylindrical package on his desk. It's wrapped like an airline calendar but it is twice the length and far bulkier. Larson had handed it to Soderlind before leaving Renton.

"I'm just curious," you comment. "What's inside?"

"Instrumentation plans for the Boeing 747," Soderlind grins. "You know, the jumbo jet we'll be flying by 1970. We wanted to take a look at what the boys in the blueprint room dreamed up for this baby's cockpit."

His eyes sparkle as he fondles the long package.

"That 747, now. Seven hundred thousand pounds of gross takeoff weight, at least ten stewardesses, eleven lavatories, and six galleys—and Boeing says she'll handle as easily as the 727. What an acceptance flight *that* will be!"

The public's view of a scheduled airline's operations can be compared to what one sees when he looks at an iceberg. Only one eighth of a berg is visible. The same is true of commercial aviation. A passenger comes in contact with skycaps, ticket agents, and stewardesses. His visual view of an airliner is limited to a glimpse of the plane as he boards, then the inside of the cabin, the pretty faces of the cabin attendants and the sometimes overly hectic procedure of retrieving his baggage.

What he does not see is what has been done to assure him of a safe flight. He has every right in the world to take safety for granted. He should feel complete confidence in crew, both cockpit and cabin. He should assume without a second thought that the plane on which he is flying has been carefully, scrupulously tested and maintained. He should relax in the knowledge that a massive, enormously complicated and expensive air traffic control system is keeping his aircraft safely separated from other planes.

It is reasonable to assume, however, that the majority of passengers do not have a total sense of security about flying. The volume of commercial air travel has mushroomed. Ten years ago 40 million Americans flew the nation's scheduled airlines. In 1969, the total surpassed the 180 million mark and by 1975, according to the most conservative estimates, at least 330 million persons will use U.S. scheduled air transportation. But it is still a pretty good bet that acceptance of the airplane has not necessarily been accompanied by a drastic lessening of fear.

It is my firm belief, gleaned from more than twenty years of close contact with the airline industry, that lack of knowledge is the prime reason behind fear of flying—a lack of knowledge about the "other ⅞ths of the iceberg." The little glimpse of an airline acceptance flight was just one example, actually a comparatively minor example, but typical of airline safety practices.

What you will read in the following pages will be no sugarcoating, no whitewash job, no viewing through rose-colored glasses. There are serious areas of weakness in air safety. But the accomplishments have too often been obscured by the black headlines accompanying a fatal crash, by critics who get more attention when they emphasize the negative while ignoring the positive, by Congressmen who use the rarity of an air disaster for personal publicity and uninformed concern that borders on the phony. Commercial aviation has enough problems without also having to combat falsehoods, scare stories, unfair accusations bordering on libel and—most important of all—an abysmal failure on the part of carping critics to acknowledge aviation's achievements even as they attack its failures.

No one in the airline or manufacturing industries, no government official concerned with aviation safety, resents an attack motivated by honest concern involving known areas of safety weaknesses and vulnerability. Those of us who admire commercial aviation, who treasure its past, who promote its present and who believe in its future, are simultaneously not unaware of its faults. A mistake in aviation is akin to an error committed in a professional football game. A boner in the latter means six points for the other team. A boner in aviation can mean death. There is no room in commercial aviation for the alibi. But there is considerable room for explanations of mistakes made, for searching examination of what caused the mistake, and for determined efforts to keep the mistake from ever being committed again.

Someone—I wish I knew his name, for it is more of an axiom than a mere quote—once wrote that "Experience is the name you give to the mistakes you made yesterday."

This aptly sums up aviation's search for greater safety. In telling that story, it is only too easy to dwell so heavily on the mistakes that the story is warped out of perspective. For every step backward, for every failure to take a step forward, aviation literally has sprinted a mile ahead.

No accident, fatal or nonfatal, is ever condoned; unless it was an act of God, it stemmed from somebody doing something wrong—on the drawing board of an aircraft designer, in the cockpit, in a hangar where a mechanic got careless or in an airline front office where an executive decision amounted to a calculated risk involving safety. But dwell on this one statistic: for every fatal crash involving a U.S. scheduled airliner in the past five years, there have been approximately 1.7 million routine flights that took off and landed in routine safety—often under weather conditions that would have grounded an airliner only a decade ago. Add to this the fact that virtually all of those 1.7 million flights were completed faster, more comfortably, and with far greater efficiency than any passenger could have experienced ten years before.

Somebody must have been doing something right. And *this*, too, is the story of commercial aviation—a far more important story, if less dramatic, than the story of mistakes. Most books written about air safety, however well-meaning or well-intentioned, have done a disservice by concentrating on the latter. So do most newspaper articles and so do the occasional statements and/or speeches made by Congressmen on the subject of air safety. Obviously 1.7 million safe flights don't warrant headlines or several pages in the Congressional Record. But the overemphasis put on the one accident per 1.7 million flights inevitably results in public distrust, fear, and even avoidance of air travel.

Najeeb E. Halaby, one of the most intelligent, personable, and devoted men who ever entered government service, made this statement when he headed the Federal Aviation Agency (now Federal Aviation Administration):

> "At base, safety—the absence of hazard or danger—is a subjective, relative quality. What is one man's safety may be another's hazard. Each has his own version. Safety, then, lies in the eyes of the beholder . . . Aviation depends on the public—on customers at the ticket window—no matter what the statistician may say, or the aviation writer, or the administrator of the FAA—for our common purpose, there is one all-important truth. The airplane is as safe as the man in the street thinks it is.
>
> "We face then the severest judge of all. There is nothing that mitigates the judgment of this man on the street. He gives no attention to the obstacles that are being overcome. He cares not for the many heroic 'saves' of our airline pilots or the controllers. He is unaware of the exacting care of our aviation me-

chanics. None of these stays with him. His judgment is as mercurial and emotional as the headlines of a daily paper. And his judgment, arising as it does out of fear and excitement and haste, demands of our transport industry nothing less than a lengthy period of operations free of disaster and death."

The growth of faith in air transportation has been incredible, surpassing the fondest hopes of those in the industry. Five years ago, only 10 percent of the nation's population had flown in a scheduled airliner. By 1969, more than 45 percent of all Americans had taken air trips. But this remarkable increase still leaves a sizable percentage of those who have never flown—for reasons varying from fares to fear. It is the latter group which concerns this writer.

It was mentioned earlier that more than 180 million Americans used scheduled air transportation in 1969 and the figure for 1970 is heading for 200 million. But these totals, however impressive, are somewhat misleading. The 180 million represent tickets sold, not individual passengers. Most air travelers take more than one flight a year. The most recent estimate (a 1968 Gallup poll conducted for TWA) of actual number of Americans who have, at one time or another, flown commercially was 51 million. This leaves about 61 million adult U.S. citizens who have never flown at all. With 70,000 new airline passengers boarding daily, 60 percent of the adult population will have taken an airline trip by 1970 and the number of non-air travelers will have dwindled to around 40 million—but still a large number, and a total that must inevitably involve fear as a major deterrent.

There have been numerous market studies of the flying and nonflying public, but with air travel expanding so fast most of them are out of date before their ink dries. One statistic has remained fairly valid, however: only about 15 percent of the total passengers take approximately 50 percent of the flights. This fact is due largely to the use of the airlines by businessmen, who comprise about 80 percent of the so-called "heavy fliers" market—Americans who make at least five air trips annually. Again, these percentages may be not only outmoded but meaningless in another few years because of the surge in first-time passengers. The airlines' youth, military, and family fares have introduced millions of young Americans to air travel, and these, presumably, will use scheduled air transportation when their careers are settled and their earnings assured. But use of the airlines still does not negate fear; fear or at least real nervousness is known to be present even among those who fly regularly, and it also is a factor in reducing the number of trips a person may make each year as well as keeping Americans off airplanes in the first place. (1)

A survey made by Louis Harris a few years ago (for American Airlines) asked more than 25,000 persons in 5,500 households—a good-sized sampling of both regular air travelers and infrequent passengers—why they fly.

Speed was cited as the primary attraction—by a whopping 67 percent. Comfort was another major reason, with 66 percent mentioning such air travel advantages as more relaxing, cleaner, and less tiring. More time at destination and less time away from home was cited by 47 percent. Such items as attentive stewardesses, service, safety, and economy were relatively far down on the list. And the top three primary reasons actually involved speed as the dominant factor. Safety was mentioned by only 17 percent, indicating the presence of some fear even among those who utilize air transportation. (2)

Strangely enough, there have been virtually no extensive surveys made on the subject of fear of flying. In all the traveling by air I do, however (about forty flights a year), I have yet to meet a passenger who would not admit to some nervousness, and I have talked to many who confess they are afraid even though they fly as often as I do. It is safe to say that all the comforting statistics in the world are not capable of reducing the element of fear to any appreciable extent. In other words, most people fly even though they *are* afraid.

Why a fear of flying?

It is, as I said before, illogical if one weighs the chances of involvement in an airliner crash against the chances of injury or death in such prosaic pastimes as driving a car, taking a bath, riding a bicycle, cleaning guns, or sailing in a pleasure boat. All of the above have more annual fatalities than the death toll in scheduled air transportation. More people were killed in pleasure-boating accidents in 1967, for example, than in *all* aircraft crashes combined— 1,308 in boats and 1,300 in private, business, and common-carrier airplanes.

Fear of flying *is* understandable, for the air is an unfamiliar dimension and anything unfamiliar can breed fear. But it also is illogical, because many of us fear it merely because it is unfamiliar and yet blithely accept far greater exposure to danger simply because the source is familiar. The automobile is a perfect example. Millions of Americans every day step into a car that is potential disaster on wheels, deliberately ignoring such hazards as worn tires, faulty windshield wipers, tired shock absorbers, burned-out or dirty headlights, and—most important of all—they drive that car with only a fraction of the skill that the greenest, newest airline pilot displays at the controls of a transport plane.

In 1969, a national vehicle safety check involving more than one million automobiles disclosed unsafe conditions in more than one-fourth of the cars examined. Tires, turn signals, brakes, windshield wipers, headlights, and rear lights were the items most frequently mentioned and all were traced to maintenance neglect. Driving a car with bad brakes would be, to an airline, the equivalent of dispatching a jet with inoperative thrust reversers.

Many who fear flying are prone to argue that "it's awful to be sitting back in an airliner cabin, knowing that if something goes wrong I can't do a damned thing about it. At least if a driver encounters an emergency, he can act himself without depending on somebody else."

True, but that "somebody else"—the airline pilot—is a superbly trained individual whose instincts and reactions are as quick as a cobra's strike. If motorists were exposed to the testing given an airline pilot, the highways would be denuded.

Critics of the yardstick the airlines use for judging their safety record—fatalities per 100 million passenger miles flown—love to suggest that a better yardstick would involve time exposure to accidents. If hours of exposure rather than miles traveled were used, they argue, the airliner would come out a poor safety second to the family automobile. In other words, because a jet can travel 600 miles in the same time an automobile covers not more than 60, it is fairer to compare the chances for death while flying 100 hours with the same 100 hours in your car.

Actually, it is almost impossible to arrive at an accurate comparison because airline mileage figures are exact, whereas private automobile mileage can only be an estimate. But if mileage is not a good yardstick, let's use another—namely, the number of times you step into your automobile compared to the number of airline flights that occur. The latter figure already has been cited—1.7 million flights for every fatal crash. Does anyone imagine, regardless of how good a driver he is (or thinks he is), that he could make 1.7 million automobile trips without having a serious accident? There are comparatively few drivers in the United States with perfect safety records. There are even fewer who can expect to go through their lives without getting involved in at least one serious accident. Yet if we use the U.S. airline safety record for 1967, an average year in the jet age, safety-wise, it would take a person flying steadily for twenty-four hours a day a total of more than eighty years before he could expect to be fatally injured in a crash.

The "nobody walks away from a crash" conviction is a major source of flying fear, but this too is somewhat illogical; very few motorists walk away from an automobile accident in which impact occurs at 50 or 60 miles an hour, a statistic which bothers pitifully few drivers. Plus the fact that there *are* survivors in approximately 60 percent of crashes.

Admittedly, the usual yardstick of fatalities per 100 million miles has statistical weaknesses—for one thing, it refers to revenue passenger deaths only and usually does not include crew. Nor does it include deaths in crashes caused by sabotage, although deliberate murder is not a fair input if we are judging an *accident* rate. So, ponder another yardstick—simple mileage traveled.

Take the airlines' fatal accident rate for any of the past five years and apply it to mileage. You would have to fly at least 250 million miles before you could expect to be involved in a fatal crash. You would have to travel only about 40 million miles in an automobile. That would make the commercial plane more than six times safer than the automobile.

Hours? The U.S. jet fatality rate in 1967 was one fatal accident for every 950,000 hours flown. Again, there is no comparative rate for automobiles because it is impossible to arrive at the precise number of total hours driven. But judging from the daily automobile death toll, let alone holiday deaths, it does not seem unreasonable to assume that there is more than one fatal automobile accident for every 950,000 hours spent on the nation's roads—when annual automobile fatalities themselves invariably exceed 40,000 (they surpassed 53,000 in 1967, 1968 and 1969).

(This observer is convinced that the automobile-vs-airliner argument has reached the point where husbands and wives might well consider driving to the airport in separate cars and then taking the same plane instead of the other way around. In the course of researching this book, I completed a 9,000-mile routine trip by air and then had three near-accidents driving home from the airport.)

Let us grant the contention of critics that it *is* possible at least to estimate the time exposure ratio of airplane-vs-automobile. Making the obvious assumption that the hours in which automobiles are driven far outstrip the hours in which airliners are flown, the critics claim that your own car is 30 percent safer than a transport plane! In other words, for every accidentless hour you spend in a plane you could spend three hours in an automobile.

Unfortunately, no set of statistics is entirely reliable—figures can be twisted or interpreted to fit almost any point of view, to buttress any side of an argument. So let us ask just one question: If flying is 30 percent more dangerous than driving the family car, why do insurance companies —the most cold-blooded, impersonal, and objective statisticians in the world—charge airline pilots exactly the same rates for life insurance as persons in such tame occupations as clerking, law, or even driving a taxicab?

Remember that if one buys this time exposure logic, one also must accept the fact that an airline pilot flies up to 75 hours a month, which happens to be double the exposure of a passenger who makes one round-trip transcontinental flight a week. If 75 hours a month are spent in a mode of transportation truly 30 percent more dangerous than the automobile, an airline pilot would be paying far higher premiums for life insurance. There are several professions deemed hazardous enough to warrant higher insurance rates, among them being those of the dock worker, lumberjack, jockey, and—believe it or not—bartender! Before 1937, insurance companies refused even to sell life insurance at any premium to pilots. Significantly, after 1937 their premium rates kept dropping steadily in direct proportion to the decreasing airline fatality rate until today a doctor pays higher premiums than a transport pilot.

There is another time exposure facet for which no statistics are available but which stems from plain common sense. How many times in the course of, say, a four- or five-hour automobile trip have you been forced to take some kind of emergency or evasive action to avoid an accident? Putting it another way, how many times does your blood pressure soar or your heart pound momentarily during virtually any drive into heavy traffic or high-speed freeway driving? It is safe to say that the frequency is far more than what an airline pilot encounters. And there *is* one statistic which bears this out factually: in 1968, 99.99970 percent of more than 5.3 million scheduled flights in the United States were completed in *total* routineness, without a semblance of even a minor incident or potential trouble.

In other words, those who feel safe in an automobile and petrified in an airliner might stop to consider the number of times risk occurs during every hour spent on a highway compared to an hour in the air. This is accident exposure reduced to its simplest terms.(3)

As former FAA Administrator Halaby pointed out, all the statistics and/or logic available are not sufficient to quell fear on the part of the public. It is bad enough that the average person is naturally nervous to begin with. Add to this the psychological shock of the occasional crash, plus what he reads or hears about the alleged or factual loopholes in air safety, and it is a wonder that air travel has grown as fast as it has. This is the real damage uninformed or false criticism accomplishes.

Can anything be done to reduce or even eliminate fear of flying?

A few years ago, eight leading psychiatrists, psychologists, and sociologists held a panel discussion on this subject of such vital interest to the airline industry. Representatives of the Air Transport Association and individual carriers attended, although they were not allowed to participate except to answer specific questions or discuss certain points raised by the panelists themselves—and only at the invitation of the moderator.

The eight panelists all had national and international reputations in their respective fields. It would have been difficult to select a group of higher professional standing. Before the seminar, the members received briefing material in the form of a background memorandum. The participants were briefed on previous fear surveys and what they have shown as to causes of fear; what the industry has done in the past to solve the fear problem, and statistical data on the composition of the air travel market.

The seminar was in general agreement with the most commonly accepted sources of fear—such factors as claustrophobia, fear of falling, fear of height, belief that no one survives a crash, fear of losing contact with the ground, etc.

But in acknowledging these various factors as primary causes of non-flying, the panelists were virtually unanimous in their belief that too little is known about the whole subject. They considered current and available data inadequate, incomplete, and possibly outdated. It was significant that perhaps 80 percent of the two-day discussion covered fears on the part of those who *do* fly. In discussing how the airlines can influence those who *do not*, the participants kept emphasizing their collective conviction that nobody really knows very much about this sizable segment of the public and its anti-flying motivations, and that much research lies ahead before a definite and major campaign can be waged in this area.

While the panelists expressed agreement with the usual and most obvious sources of fear cited above, they also raised some other interesting possibilities. For example:

—The nature of a crash and its attendant drama may have a tremendous effect. Such accidents as those which killed a number of prominent citizens of Atlanta, and the U.S. skating team tragedy, probably have a more shocking and lasting effect than the average accident.

—A very underrated problem may be the effects of an accident on those who knew the victims involved. One panelist suggested that if a hundred persons are killed in a crash, a fear factor is spread directly to at least five thousand "proximities"—the relatives, friends, and even acquaintances of those who died.

—The natural tendency of a person to exaggerate a flying incident is probably a minor but very real source of transmitting unjustified fears. The average passenger, particularly male, is very likely to "blow up" an experience from what it actually was—routine—into a close brush with death. Inasmuch as civil aviation inevitably encounters routine "non-normal" incidents daily, there is no way to judge the extent of this bragging habit in spreading anti-flying prejudice and fear.

27

—There may be a class structure to fear of flying, and this would involve apprehension not about death but of social circumstances. Do many persons refuse to fly because they do not know what to wear or are worried about not "looking right" in the midst of other passengers? Do they feel "planes aren't for the likes of me"? Is there even a "fear of destination"? Several panelists questioned whether airline advertising that concentrates on glamorous destinations actually may contribute to a class fear category. This was one of the major areas in which the participants agreed there should be more research, in the belief that the industry may have to work out separate campaigns to aim at different class levels.

The panelists raised a number of important questions for which there were no ready answers.

Is it possible that fear of flying is most prevalent among those who fly a little? Who may say "I fly four or five times a year and that's enough because if I fly any more my number's likely to be up"? Who regard commercial aviation as a giant Russian roulette game with "forty-five thousand chambers," as one participant put it?

What do people think makes a flight dangerous? Are they more afraid of landings and takeoffs than of flying at 35,000 feet? Would they rather experience engine failure or get stacked up over New York? Why do passengers choose certain seats? Do any deliberately sit by emergency exits? How many wives won't fly on the same planes with their husbands? What is the extent of the "bragging" factor? What are the specific effects of an accident or serious incident on fear in terms of cancellations?

These were just some of the questions and potentially rich research areas raised by the seminar. The participants felt that available data and perhaps much of the industry's current thinking is based on research that is vague, rhetorical and superficial—almost a grab bag of ideas and beliefs stemming from totally inadequate information.

One of the most significant and surprising views expressed by the panel was its own lack of knowledge about air safety. These were highly intelligent men, most of them frequent or at least occasional air travelers, and presumably with a much sharper realization of the safety situation than the average person.

Yet the panelists expressed unanimous amazement at the safety statistics furnished them as part of the pre-seminar background material. They said they had no idea air travel was so safe.

A great deal of time was spent discussing recent experiments which demonstrated that it is possible to manipulate emotions, such as fear, by establishing cognizance of a given situation. In somewhat simpler terms, the panelists suggested it is theoretically possible to substitute excitement for fear—for example, convincing a passenger that a takeoff is thrilling, not frightening.

Some of this discussion wandered a bit into the wild blue yonder. One panelist proposed that the airlines stop playing soft music before takeoffs because it actually contributed to fear. Music that is spirited, peppy, or even martial, he suggested, would achieve the substitution of excitement for fear.

Probably this distinguished panelist was not being serious on this score, but the panelists were most serious about changing the atmosphere aboard planes as a means of reducing the fear factor.

It was agreed, for example, that keeping passengers busy tends to allay or at least hide fear. It was noted that a mother being kept busy with a traveling baby never seems to get airsick—and airsickness often can be traced to fear. In-flight movies were brought up, and the panelists expressed great interest in this device as an anti-fear weapon. When a TWA representative was invited to comment on this possibility, he pointed out that the carrier's movies were designed mainly to alleviate boredom, not fear—which prompted the panel's response that alleviating boredom might alleviate fear.

In this respect, the panelists felt there is a wide field for experimentation on creating a more favorable atmosphere not only in planes themselves but even in airports. They did not agree on methods to achieve this atmosphere, merely on the need for it. For example, they considered the interior of an average transport a possible source of apprehension in its very layout—the long tube or cave idea. It was suggested that the airlines take a single jet and try out a new interior design—one that has the necessary economic capacity but also provides more of a social, club car atmosphere.

One specific suggestion for this cabin layout experiment: a compartmentalized aircraft with separate sections for those who like to drink, those who like to walk around, those who want to read and/or be alone, those who want to smoke, etc. The panelists conceded that cabin revisions are subject to the need for good load factors, but claimed that the airlines have more flexibility in aircraft interiors than they imagine. At any rate, an experimental interior was one of the seminar's proposals for acquiring more data on fear of flying and how to combat it. (The new Boeing 747 "jumbo jet" with its separate lounges plus galleys and toilets in the middle of the cabin aisle instead of next to the walls is more of an actuality than an experiment in elimination of the tube effect.)

The possibility of extending this "atmospheric attack" to airports also was admittedly theoretical, but one that the panelists believed would warrant experimentation. Putting movie theaters into major airports was one idea. Attractive, educational, and interesting airline displays was another— such as a typical cockpit layout, a cabin mockup, a display on how air traffic control works, or even a motion picture depicting the experience of flight.

As in the case of the suggested experimental interior, there was no definite agreement on what should or could be done at airports. But there *was* agreement on the need for doing something to alleviate preflight fears on the part of new or infrequent passengers, or perhaps the fears of non-flying persons who might come to an airport.

Actually, the panel acknowledged that in many ways the jets have achieved much along these lines—through their lack of interior noise, their cleanliness, speed, vibrationless operation, etc. But the seminar emphasized that the jets have offered no cure-all and in themselves may have raised new fear problems through unfamiliar noises and operating techniques. The panelists broached the thought that many situations which are routine to airline people are capable of causing concern, fear, and apprehension on the part of passengers. Throughout all this discussion ran the recurring theme that it is, indeed, possible to transform these concerns into more favorable attitudes.

The seminar was in complete and rather significant agreement on the role that pilots can play in achieving this "transformation." Judicious, carefully handled cabin PA announcements, the panelists said, could be a major tool to the extent of warranting an airline effort to enlist pilot aid in a campaign. But they had these words of caution:

First, the panelists suggested, there should be an inventory of what can occur during a flight that causes fear. Pilot PA announcements should be handled with such an inventory in mind.

Second, the panelists warned, there is the danger of too much pilot information backfiring: one participant suggested the possibility of a "methinks the gentleman doth protest too much" kind of reaction among passengers—namely, "If he's doing all this reassuring, maybe I've really got something to worry about."

Third, it was suggested that nothing can be more frightening than a cabin PA which is unclear or garbled. Several panelists quite seriously commented that improved PA systems, put into the hands of pilots made aware of the effectiveness of good PA announcements, are most essential.

Despite these reservations, the panelists regarded adequate flight information from the flight deck as very promising. They even brought up personal experiences of their own to cite their own reactions. One told of a pilot who explained to his passengers the reasons behind a decision to move away from the ramp and get into a long line of planes waiting for takeoff clearance rather than just waiting at the ramp for the traffic jam to clear. Another recounted several instances where a pilot advised of a fifteen-to twenty-minute delay but was able to take off in five or ten minutes—suggesting a neat little psychological trick of getting passengers to anticipate the maximum inconvenience, then pleasantly surprising them with the minimum.

Only a pilot, the panel emphasized, can explain immediately situations that cause fear and perhaps even instill long-standing prejudice against flying. There may even be room for a good cockpit sense of humor in certain circumstances; one panelist cited the case of sudden loss of altitude which brought from the flight deck a good-natured "Whoops!" This was not exactly a scientific explanation for the drop, but it was the type of deliberate wisecracking which the panel felt to be most apropos on some occasions.

Some panelists went so far as to suggest that passengers might be allowed to listen to takeoff and landing clearances, or the reading of a checklist—if not over PA systems, perhaps through individual earphones.

While some of this may seem petty to an airline—or a pilot—it should be emphasized that the panel regarded it as essential that pilots give passengers an image of complete responsibility, and that such an image can be provided through calm, carefully worded, and judiciously timed PA information.

For that matter, the panelists pointed out that cutting down irritation is almost as important as cutting down fear, because there is some evidence that irritation is not unrelated to fear. And the seminar was agreed that lack of information is a source of irritation.

In general, the seminar reached agreement in these areas:

1. Flying is safe and most fears are unjustified.

2. No one, including the participants on this panel, is exactly sure what people are afraid of and the extent to which it prevents them from flying.

3. There are many promising avenues for the airlines to explore in reducing fear on the part of those who do fly and who would fly more if the experience of flight could be made more pleasurable and more exciting rather than frightening; the size of this group is something that should be ascertained because it may be vastly larger than anyone supposes.

4. There probably is no anti-fear campaign that will hit all targets; rather, the campaign to conquer fear and develop confidence in scheduled air transportation must take into consideration that the target categories may vary considerably, from those who have never flown to those who fly occasionally and can afford to fly more.

Point 4 underlined the seminar's belief that the fear problem actually is twofold: fear while flying and fear before flying. It also underlined the seminar's conviction that the airlines could not wage any campaign in either of these two areas without assembling more data on what fears are involved among the different audiences the industry is trying to reach.

The panelists agreed there is potentially "happy marriage" between the airline industry and psychology or psychiatry—in the sense that if the airlines really want to conquer fear, there is no shortage of professionally skilled interrogators, public opinion specialists, and scientists capable of conducting controlled experiments, all aimed at accumulating the data necessary for determining what campaign or campaigns would be most effective.

The panelists thought the airlines should be willing to spend the necessary funds on collecting such data and also should be willing to try some experiments which may seem startling or even scatterbrained until it is realized how little we know about fear. For example, several panelists favored a test to measure the output of adrenalin during such flight phases as takeoffs, landings, and turbulence.

The seminar was less sanguine about the chances of conquering fear among those who do not fly. The panelists considered this non-flying group largely inaccessible at present, with only the crudest idea of what constitutes this obviously enormous group and what constitutes its fears.

But the panelists did express the belief that the airlines have, in effect, ducked the issue of promoting safety as such—even though it was their unanimous conviction that the airlines have the right to be tremendously proud of their safety achievements. To this group of experts, the airlines' ducking of the safety promotion issue, while at the same time they were justifiably proud of their safety accomplishments, seemed completely incongruous. The seminar was agreed unanimously, in effect, that the airlines have a most salable product on which they are doing too little selling.

There were specific "selling" proposals made, such as:

—Reviving the use of pamphlets in seat backs, along the lines of American's little "This Is What Flying's All About" booklet (which several panelists praised).

—An industry-wide institutional campaign to emphasize the safety of flight (several panelists recalled American's blunt "Are You Afraid to Fly?" advertisements of several years ago and expressed wonder that the entire industry has not sponsored similar ads).

—Establishment of a central airline information office in one or two major cities on a trial basis; this would be similar to the joint train information system in which the public can dial a single, central source for information on all train schedules. (This had the most emphatic support of any proposal, with all participants agreeing that a vast segment of the public simply hasn't any idea of where to go for general airline information, and that unfamiliarity with airline operations is undoubtedly an indirect fear factor.)

—Setting up an industry speaker's bureau composed of pilots and other qualified personnel who would go out and lecture various groups on air safety, particularly women's

33

organizations; the panelists felt that the airlines have done too little to convince women of air safety.

—While the panelists were cautioned in advance not to get into the area of airline fares unless it was related to fear, the gentlemen could not refrain from expressing the view that getting more people to try flying is one answer. Thus there were a number of suggestions that the airlines revive sight-seeing flights, lower fares to attract large family or group travel, and other proposals stemming from their belief that such promotion could tap the non-flying market; in fact, the idea of experimenting with a new type of "social structure" interior, to appeal to groups or families, was related to this area. The suggestion for sight-seeing flights, incidentally, brought some mention of the success American and TWA have had with this type of promotion in recent years.

Obviously, not even this distinguished panel could come up with a definite answer to the fear problem in a day-and-a-half session. What the seminar did achieve was a realization of the enormous extent of the problem. In this respect, the panelists urged that some experimentation along the lines they suggested should proceed immediately, without waiting for the much larger task of accumulating all the necessary data on fear prior to launching any all-out attack.

Such an eventual attack, the panelists emphasized, must largely revolve around efforts to educate the public on air safety because the problem, boiled down to the simplest terminology, is simply that people don't realize how safe flying is. As one panelist phrased it:

"Fear of accidental death is not confined to flying, but in the case of flying it is a unique fear because it is based on gross misunderstanding or misinformation."

That seminar was held in 1964, and as of this writing, there were several airline-sponsored surveys under way in the areas suggested. The results will be interesting and, hopefully, valuable because there still are indications that the airlines remain extremely sensitive about safety and reluctant to mention the subject of fear.

There certainly is need for an industry-wide effort to allay fears, particularly among first-time or infrequent air passengers whose natural apprehensions are compounded by unfamiliar sounds and sights—such as their initial look at the wings of a four-engine jet oscillating noticeably even in mild turbulence. Few if any of these frightened persons realize that the flexing ability of a jet's wings actually is a safety measure in that they absorb strains and stresses rather than resist them. All airlines should adopt TWA's practice of telling passengers in advance that they will experience certain sounds—the noise of the landing gear being raised or lowered and the thunder of jet engines going into reverse on landing.

Several major airlines have fear-easing information in magazines or pamphlets carried in seatbacks—American's "This Is Your Captain Speaking" being an excellent example of a regular column published in its monthly in-flight magazine. Western is toying with a plan to have its ticket agents ascertain whether a customer is a first-time flier; if this is the case, the agents would enclose in the ticket envelope a little brochure telling the passenger what to expect, some pertinent facts on air safety, and other information designed to reassure as well as educate.

In 1967, Pacific Air Lines—a local service carrier—hired humorist Stan Freberg to compose a series of advertisements aimed at the "afraid to fly" contingent. The first one was a humdinger that shocked the entire industry. It was captioned: "HEY THERE—YOU WITH THE SWEAT IN YOUR PALMS." The text carried the surprising message that pilots, too, occasionally have sweat in their palms, but don't worry, flying is still pretty safe.

Freberg might as well have come out foursquare in favor of communism, sin, and LSD consumption. The series was so controversial that it resulted in widespread industry condemnation and caused the eventual resignations of several top Pacific officials, as well as the subsequent retirement of Mr. Freberg from the airline advertising field—by request. Pacific explained, rather lamely, that it merely wanted people to notice the airline; there was no intent to scare anyone.

At the risk of alienating many airline friends, it is the opinion of this observer that while Freberg went a little too far, his intentions were entirely honorable, praiseworthy, and rather refreshing. The airlines have come a long way since they used to send employees to the scene of a crash armed with pails of whitewash—to obliterate the name of the airline if it was still visible on the wreckage. But most of them persist in what can be classed only as an "ostrich attitude." No carrier can defend a fatal crash, which is the worst publicity possible. But few if any airlines react to the wild guessing, uninformed accusations, and harmful speculation that inevitably follow a crash—particularly from Congressmen. It is not enough that the industry relies on the press to scotch rumors and answer false charges—the press is sometimes as guilty as Congress.

Curiously enough, the airlines sometimes react violently to incidents far less harmful than those perpetrated by certain lawmakers and a minority of news media. A case in point was the 1964 crash test staged by the FAA and the Flight Safety Foundation in Phoenix. On April 24, the FAA and FSF deliberately wrecked an old DC-7 crammed with impact-measuring instruments, dummies, and crash survival equipment.

The DC-7, which used to fly for United, was sent down a special runway that was nothing but a deadly obstacle course—with telephone poles and mounds of earth strategically placed to simulate a typical takeoff accident. Spectacular was the only word for the test, which was well covered by all news media. In fact, it turned out to be more spectacular than anyone expected. A last-second tailwind, just as the plane was released via remote control for its plunge down the booby-trapped runway, increased the impact speed to 20 miles an hour above the planned speed. Damage to the aircraft and its interior was considerably more than the engineers expected—and the pictures were correspondingly more startling.

There was no disagreement on the value of the experiment. But there was a blistering quarrel over the publicity it received. Briefly, the airlines believed the FAA did air travel no favor when it gave the news media free access to the motion-picture and still shots of the crash. The movies, shown widely on television, were pretty rough. There were slow-motion color films of the plane bursting into flames, the cockpit disintegrating as it crunched into a small hill, dummies in the cabin being tossed about wildly and crushed by collapsing seats—the airlines feared that such vivid pictorial material was hardly calculated to win friends for flying or influence potential passengers.

Airline officials complained privately and unofficially after the FAA released the films and photographs. But their resentment came out in the open when the President of the Air Transport Association, Stuart G. Tipton, disclosed he had written a protesting letter to then FAA chief Halaby. Halaby's answer, in effect, was a blunt "go fly your kite."

He said the public had a perfect right to know what the FAA was doing about improving the chances for survival in a landing or takeoff accident. Tipton then replied that the airlines were not objecting to press coverage of the Phoenix tests, but rather to the propriety of a Federal agency handing out gruesome pictures that could only "scare the daylights" out of people already afraid to fly.

Many airline officials felt that some of the more shocking pictures of the Arizona test actually cost them not only potential customers but solidified the fears of those millions who fly only when they have to.

"As for the non-flying segment of the population," said one airline executive, "the average 'I won't fly' citizen, frightened when he reads headlines about crashes, must be even more perturbed when he sees actual films of a crash, interior as well as exterior. Hell, I was a little scared myself."

The FAA's side of the controversy was that the airlines were being oversensitive. First, the agency argued, the public was well conditioned in advance to the fact that the Phoenix crash was a scientific experiment involving an old plane and presumably accepted even the most sensational pictures in that spirit. Second, the overall effect of all the publicity, including the films and photographs, was one of reassurance—it made the public aware of how much effort is going into the task of making air travel safer. In fact, the FAA insisted, the spectacular aspects of the test may have contributed to that reassurance.

There probably is something to be said for both airline and FAA viewpoints. The airlines had some justification in pointing out that the FAA by law is entrusted with contributing to the advancement of commercial aviation—and that scaring people doesn't classify as an advancement. The tests *could* have been run without publicity and achieved the same scientific results. There was no doubt that the films were brutally effective; I know several friends who claim they remember the movie shots every time they board an airliner.

But the FAA also was justified in feeling that the airlines frequently have given the impression that even discussing air safety problems is bad for business—sort of an "if we don't talk about it, the problem may go away" attitude. It was interesting to note that the industry was not unanimous in scolding the FAA. W. A. Patterson, then Chairman of the Board of United Air Lines, held that the Phoenix tests (there

37

were two staged crashes, the second involving a Constellation the following September) were beneficial in two ways: they contributed to flight safety, and the attendant publicity in turn contributed to public reassurance.

Patterson, who has since retired from an active role in aviation, was one of the few airline presidents who constantly chided his colleagues for ducking discussion of safety issues and problems. C. R. Smith of American was another —he publicly promoted and defended the Lockheed Electra when other Electra operators were taking the name of the maligned propjet out of their advertisements. To men like Patterson and Smith, the publicity given an air safety experiment was at least preferable to the attention given a real crash—particularly one in which emergency evacuation weaknesses cost lives that might have been saved.

In truth, the industry does not have to hide its head, avoid mention of safety whether negative or positive, or apologize for its record. ATA president Tipton once defined safety as "the art of reducing risk to the least possible chance of occurrence." That is precisely what the aviation community —airlines, government, and manufacturers—have accomplished with fantastic strides. Granted there have been stumbles and falls. It also can be conceded air travel could be safer. But in making that concession, it is too easy to forget the achievements of the past, the efforts being exerted in the present, and magnificent, almost unbelievable goals of the future.

And thus it is time to examine, dispassionately, the miracle wrought in the past decade—the first ten years of the jet age.

2. THE FIRST TEN YEARS

On October 26, 1958, a Pan American World Airways Boeing 707 took off from Idlewild International Airport (now Kennedy) bound for Paris and literally got the jet revolution under way.

The proud British might regard this as sophistry, inasmuch as their Comets were flying passengers as far back as May of 1952. But the Comets, stricken with a fatal structural weakness, were grounded two years later and did not carry a passenger again until October 4, 1958, after they had undergone drastic structural changes. The resumption of Comet service over the North Atlantic preceded the Pan Am inaugural jet flight by twenty-two days and to the British went the chronological honors. But while the Comet was the technological pioneer, the larger and faster Boeing 707 and the subsequent Douglas DC-8 were the planes truly responsible for the jet revolution.

And revolution is the only applicable word to what has transpired in the past decade. It was poetic justice that the first scheduled flight of an American-made jetliner was from New York to Paris. Forty-four years before the inauguration of New York–Paris jet service, a famous American penned these words:

> It is a bare possibility that a one-man machine without a float and favored by a wind say of fifteen miles an hour might succeed in getting across the Atlantic. But such an attempt would be the height of folly. When one comes to increase the size of the craft, the possibility rapidly fades away. This is be-

39

cause of the difficulties of carrying sufficient fuel . . . it will readily be seen, therefore, why the Atlantic flight is out of the question.

The author of that pessimistic peek into the future was Orville Wright, a gallant aviation pioneer but a poor prophet. Exactly thirteen years later, Charles Lindbergh did what Orville Wright (and quite a few others) said was impossible. And forty years after Lindbergh's historic flight, there was a scheduled jetliner crossing the Atlantic once every ten minutes during peak traffic hours, carrying more than 100 passengers at 600 miles an hour at altitudes of up to 40,000 feet.

Transatlantic traffic alone totals about 3 million passengers a year and the jets are flying 11 persons for every one who travels by ship. It was the jet that made ocean flights routine, so routine that it is easy to become jaded toward the enormous technical achievements involved. Orville Wright worried about fuel capacity. A Boeing 707 or DC-8 taking off on an overseas flight burns more fuel in the first three minutes than Lindbergh did in thirty-three hours. One engine on a jet transport weighs more than the entire *Spirit of St. Louis*. And when Wright said the Atlantic could be crossed only by a plane carrying a single man, he never could foresee that a fully loaded jetliner's wings would be capable of supporting the weight of 102 pounds for every square foot of wing area—which amounts to carrying a load of automobiles stacked as high as the Washington Monument on each wing.

The jets figuratively shrank the world by 40 percent, cruising at speeds made possible by only four engines; if engineers wanted to fly a piston-engine plane at 600 miles an hour, they would have to install 40 power plants. A jet is so perfectly streamlined that dirt on the fuselage increases fuel consumption by nearly two pounds per nautical mile. On a New York–Rome flight, a dirty airplane would cost an airline 1,000 gallons of extra fuel.

The jet has changed travel habits to such an extent that it produced the coining of a new phrase—jet set. It is more than just a phrase. There was a young woman in Washington, D.C., who flew to Rome every other week to see her fiancé, while he flew to Washington on alternate weekends. Ditto a San Francisco lawyer engaged to a girl in Honolulu. He took a jet to Hawaii one weekend and she flew to San Francisco the next.

It is not unusual these days for couples to fly from one city to another just for dinner and a show, returning home the same night. In Miami two winters ago, a couple of lifeguards got bored with all the sunshine, caught a plane to New Hampshire, spent a weekend skiing, and were back at work on the beach Monday morning.

"Instant mobility" is one name given to the phenomenon of the jet age. That is what Stuart G. Tipton of ATA called it in a speech. He was referring to the growing acceptance of air travel thanks to the jet—growing so fast that even the airlines are stunned. In 1939, the U.S. airlines flew 1.7 million passengers during the entire year. They now carry 3 million every week.

Traffic in the first decade of the jets has soared 135.7 percent—from 56 million passengers in 1958 to more than 180 million in 1969. The U.S. population is growing by 7,000 persons daily, but that is 63,000 less than the number of new passengers who boarded the airlines every day in 1969. The latter figure could be hopelessly out of date by the time you read this; as recently as 1966, the total of new passengers daily was only 10,000. The jet revolution's impact on just one American city—Cleveland, Ohio—will underscore its multiplying germination: Cleveland generated more traffic in 1967 than *all* the U.S. airlines carried during 1940. One forecast predicts that the nation's scheduled carriers will be flying 500 million passengers annually by 1980.

In Denver, city officials looked into various crystal balls in the early days of the jet age and decided to modernize their airport to handle 6 million passengers by 1975. The airport in 1968, one year before it was finished, already was serving 6 million passengers. When the jets began service in 1958, they were operating in and out of only 2 domestic airports. By the end of 1967, jets were serving more than 180 airports.

From every side come indications that Americans are treating air travel almost as casually as they do the automobile. One example: only a few years ago, the overwhelming majority of reservations made for business flights were booked at least one week in advance. Now most business reservations are made only a day or two before the intended flight, and a significant number are made on the same day.

Business travel still accounts for most air trips. But the percentage is dropping steadily, thanks to the avalanche of special promotional fares appealing to families and youths. United Air Lines, in fact, reported that in 1968 more than half its passengers flew for reasons unrelated to business—the first reversal of the historical pattern. Only one year after the airlines introduced the family fare, the new rate was producing more than 25 percent of their coach revenues—an almost miraculous market penetration in such a short time. And no wonder. It is possible to fly a family of five coast-to-coast for $77 per person; just try budgeting the same trip for the same number of persons by car.

Another aspect of the jet revolution is that travel is now getting priority over other so-called luxury items in family expenditures. Many families already have that second car, fairly new television sets, and a myriad of home appliances. As incomes increase, there is room in the budget for long trips that would be difficult or impossible in an automobile.

Hawaii provides a good example of the impact of jet vacation travel. In 1947, there were less than 55,000 airline passengers between California and the Islands. There now are more than 1 million a year. In 1947, Hawaii offered a total of 1,500 hotel rooms and now has more than 15,000.

Only a relative handful of Americans flew in the year 1932, when a transcontinental air trip required nearly 30 hours and 11 stops. (Today there are approximately 300 scheduled jet transcontinental trips daily carrying 20,000 passengers.) (4)

Let's look at that year 1932 . . .

When engines had to be inspected every 25 hours and overhauled every 250 hours because of their unreliability. (The modern jet engine averages 8,000 hours between overhauls, with a single overhaul costing $90,000—$40,-000 more than the price tag on a single transport plane of the thirties.)

When cancellations because of weather and mechanical troubles were so frequent that pilots carried special forms authorizing passengers to switch to railroads. (In 1968, with jets flying 80 percent of the traffic, the airlines completed 98 percent of their scheduled mileage—which added up, by the way, to an astronomical 2 billion miles.)

When the airline fatality rate was 14.96 deaths for every 100 million passenger miles flown, thanks to 16 fatal crashes—not a bad rate considering the fact that the airlines had 108 accidents that year. (In the past ten years, the U.S. airlines' fatality rate has ranged from a high of 0.76 in 1960—a rate due mostly to the Lockheed Electra's troubles at the time—to an all-time low of 0.07 in 1966. Not since 1951 has the rate gone as high as one death per 100 million miles.)

When a new copilot could be hired at 10 A.M. and be flying a regular trip in the right seat by 3 P.M. the same day. (A new pilot today goes through at least six weeks of ground school plus three weeks of flight training, and has to be retrained all over again when he shifts to different equipment or upgrades to captain. The airlines now spend $100 million annually just for flight crew training, a sum representing the industry's *entire gross* in 1940. At any given time, roughly 10 percent of an airline's pilots are in some phase of new or recurrent training.)

When all twenty-four airlines then operating in the United States offered a total of less than 700 daily flights. (A single local service airline schedules that many every day.)

When 80 percent of the 450 planes in the nation's commercial air fleet were single-engine aircraft. (The fleet now numbers approximately 2,000, about 1,100 of the aircraft being pure jets and another 400 propjets whose turbine engines are hitched to conventional propellers.)

When the country's biggest airline proudly boasted it would fly 100,000 passengers during the year. (The same airline is currently carrying that many every two days.)

When it was a rarity to see a woman on an airplane because 98 percent of air trips were for business and the average passenger load was almost entirely male. (Approximately 50 percent of today's pleasure travelers are female and one out of ten business fliers are women.)

When the pilot work force in scheduled air transportation numbered less than 700 men. (In 1969, there were 23,000 active airline pilots, who, incidentally, had a two-hundred-times-better chance of staying alive on their job than their brethren of 1932.)

When the twelve-passenger Ford Trimotor was the

queen of the nation's commercial air fleet. (Just one airline, American, has figured out that to operate its present schedules solely between New York and Chicago would require 400 Trimotors making 200 departures each way, manned by 2,400 pilots and 1,200 stewardesses and needing 400 fuel stops at both Detroit and Buffalo. And at today's jet fares, American would lose $25 per passenger operating that 400-Trimotor fleet.)

The contrast between 1932 and the present, of course, is far more dramatic than comparing the heyday of the pistons—the middle 1950s—with the jet years of the sixties. Yet even the latter comparison offers some startling items.

—The major U.S. airlines have invested more than $8 billion in *new* jet equipment during the 1966–70 period; in 1955, the entire propeller-driven fleet represented an investment of less than $1.2 billion. The $8 billion does not include jets delivered before 1966.

—In 1955, slightly more than a half cent of every airline revenue dollar went for interest payments on new piston equipment. The figure for the jet age averages four cents out of every revenue dollar.

—The price tag on the spare parts inventory for a major airline was $19 million at the start of the jet age. It is now around $60 million for the average carrier.

—The New York Port Authority pre-jet investment at Kennedy Airport was $221 million. Today it has more than $400 million invested, with Kennedy's terminal area alone covering one hundred acres more than the entire LaGuardia Airport installation, including runways.

—A DC-3 did a day's work when it flew from New York to Little Rock, Arkansas. A Constellation or DC-6 and DC-7 could get in, at the most, a one-way coast-to-coast flight. The jet's minimum workday covers a round trip between the East and West Coasts, with utilization hitting as high as seventeen hours just for passenger flights. A single Boeing 727QC (QC for "Quick Change"), which can be converted from a passenger aircraft to an all-cargo plane or back again in less than forty-five minutes, often will be flown twenty hours out of every twenty-four—the non-flying period being used for maintenance. It carries passengers by day and freight by night. During 1968, the airlines took delivery on 444 new transports—which happened to be just about the size of the entire U.S. commercial fleet in 1932. The industry's 1968-74 reequipment program amounts to $10 billion for more than 1,300 new planes. During 1968, the airlines took delivery on 2 new jets, averaging $6.5 million per aircraft, every working day of the year. The $10 billion reequipment program is even more staggering when one realizes that the airlines' net worth in 1967 was only $2.9 billion, and it is just further proof of the jet revolution's extent. In terms of that vital economic barometer, capital spending, the air transportation industry is now the nation's seventh largest.

(For those who may have become a bit blasé about large sums, even when expressed in the billions, ponder this: to get rid of $1 billion, you would have to spend $1,000 daily for 3,500 years!)

The jet age has been an employment bonanza in the nation's economy. The airline industry in 1956 had on its payrolls slightly more than 131,000 persons. By 1967 total employment had boomed to 275,000, with a 13 percent gain registered between 1966 and 1967 alone. The airlines used to be happy with a 5 percent annual gain in traffic. The average for the past five years has exceeded 15 percent. And the end does not seem to be in sight. Economists estimate that traffic will double in the next half decade—with the resulting need for another 4,000 pilots and 11,000 mechanics by 1970, not to mention what will be needed in additional ground personnel. The stewardess force alone has soared from 8,000 in 1956 to 31,000 in 1970.

The air travel surge also has sparked a corresponding boom in the manufacturing end of commercial aviation. The number of new jobs in the commercial transport field jumped 11 percent between March of 1966 and March 1967. The Air Transport Association estimates that the U.S. supersonic transport program alone will have an economic fall-out of $20 billion to $50 billion in the next five to ten years. The ATA forecast is based on the expected creation of 250,000 new jobs: 50,000 for the prime contractors, Boeing and General Electric, plus 100,000 for subcontractors, with these 150,000 new jobs creating another 10,000 positions in nonmanufacturing industries ranging from communications to real estate. ATA believes the SST project will account for one out of every 50 new civilian jobs created by 1975.

Thus the jet revolution is destined to continue, spreading

its influence and effects throughout the nation's and the world's economy. For it is not merely an American revolution; the jet has had worldwide repercussions, even in areas one might think immune to advances of commercial aviation. One example will suffice.

Any GI who fought on the island of New Guinea in World War II will remember it as a steaming, primitive pesthole that reverted to the jungle as soon as the war ended. New Guinea might seem like the most unlikely target on the planet for aviation progress. Yet today the island has 126 airports which serve 500,000 passengers a year. Scheduled airline operations in and out of New Guinea exceed 100,000 movements annually. The airplane, and the jet in particular, has metamorphosed what was for centuries a primeval land.

The jet revolution occurred because jet transportation introduced new dimensions of speed, comfort, capacity, and efficiency. But these factors would have been worthless without the most important accomplishment of all—new dimensions of safety. This is what made public acceptance of the other factors possible.

The prosaic routineness of modern air transportation has caused the unhappier memories of the past to fade. A 1936 *Fortune* magazine survey offers a stark example of how things used to be. The survey disclosed that if Americans were given a choice between a plane or a train for a journey of more than 500 miles, 75 percent would pick the train. That was the overall percentage; among the men polled, 70 percent chose the train while nearly 81 percent of the women preferred railroad travel.

Nobody blamed them, either. The Actuarial Society of America, about the same time, said an airliner was fifty-three times more dangerous than a Pullman. And commercial flying was rated eight times more hazardous than the private automobile.

Compare the *Fortune* survey with a poll conducted in 1963 by the American Newspaper Publishers Association. This time the question was: "If you were making a long trip (over one thousand miles) and flying was the cheapest way to go, would you fly or use some other means of transportation?" The results:

·—Of those who travel for business, 95 percent said they would fly.

—Among nonbusiness travelers, 92 percent picked flying.

—Among those who did not fly, 64 percent said they would fly if it were the least expensive way to travel: 23 percent preferred the automobile, and only 11 percent chose trains.

If the story of commercial aviation is one of gradual public acceptance, it also is a story of gradual improvement in safety. On a year-by-year basis, the airline fatality rate tends to fluctuate slightly. It seems fairer to measure the record at longer range—on the basis of five-year averages. Using the airlines' yardstick—fatalities per 100 million passenger miles flown—the picture is one of steady progress:

1942–46	2.10
1947–51	1.51
1952–56	.50
1957–61	.48
1962–66	.22

As Daniel Priest, vice president of public relations for ATA, put it in a speech:

"From the passenger point of view, the fatality rate is the key element in measuring the progress of airline safety. Not only has it improved, it *had* to improve. If the airlines had the same fatality rate, 5.20, that they had in 1938, the airlines last year (1967) would have had five thousand, one hundred and sixty-four fatalities instead of the two hundred and twenty-six they did have."

Note, in the five-year averages, how the safety rate improved during the 1957–66 decade. There were many who predicted a rise in the rate after jets began operating in 1958. After all, they were a completely different type of aircraft flying at speeds and altitudes never before reached by commercial transports. They were not only faster but much heavier, with unfamiliar handling characteristics that invited trouble. They were far more unforgiving than a piston-engine plane and if one did crash, the passenger load alone would have a serious effect on the airlines' own safety yardstick. A fully occupied 707 or DC-8 that crashed could involve as many fatalities as six fatal accidents involving fully loaded DC-3s.

But it just didn't happen that way. While the jets did

47

present safety problems (they *are*, without any doubt, unforgiving beasts that must be flown by the book), they also proved safer than the older planes in many respects —they are stronger, more powerful, exceptionally superior in terms of engine reliability, and their altitude capability puts them above bad weather during most portions of a flight. In the seven years between 1960 and 1967, there were 116 fatal crashes involving piston-engine planes flown by the scheduled airlines of the free world. In the same period, there were 35 fatal accidents involving jets, and 38 involving propjets. In 1969, with jets accounting for four fifths of air traffic, the fatality rate for the U.S. scheduled airlines was lower than that of trains and buses—and thirty times less than that of the private automobile.

The most comprehensive survey of jet crashes was done by Captain William Moss, a flight operations official for Pan American World Airways. It was first prepared in 1963 and later updated to include jet accidents that occurred through 1966. Moss delivered his initial paper before the Flight Safety Foundation's International Air Safety Seminar in Athens, Greece, under a rather dull title: "Special Aspects of Jet Statistics."

But the contents added up to some of the most provocative observations and conclusions ever made about safety in the jet age. What Moss did was to study the official and unofficial causes of every fatal jetliner accident between 1958 and 1967. At the time he prepared his facts and figures, there were 89 free world airlines operating jets with a total accumulation of about 15 million hours. It was a pretty good chunk of basic source material and Moss even loaded the dice *against* the jets. First, he avoided using the much-criticized statistical base of fatalities per 100 million passenger miles flown. He chose instead the yardstick of hours flown per fatal crash. Furthermore, he included training accidents and sabotage cases—types of crashes which are not fed into the usual safety statistics. Yet even with this more critical ruler, the jets' record was impressive.

The Moss study confirmed a little-realized achievement of the jet age: the fatal accident rate generally has declined in direct proportion to the increasing use of jets. The rate started with one fatal jet crash every 150,000 hours over the first two years—1959 and 1960. It improved dramatically to a rate of one fatal accident per 720,000 hours by 1965. Then the rate worsened to one crash for every 350,000 hours. Moss traced the increase to what safety experts term the "learning curve"—which is simply the lack of experience in operating new types of aircraft. In 1965 and 1966, there were several accidents involving the relatively new Boeing 727 and BAC-111— both so-called "second generation"—as well as the brand-new DC-9. The Boeing 727's difficulties will be treated in a later chapter; at this point, it is enough to say that the airlines cannot condone, in good faith, any learning curve. A passenger has the right to expect that all the necessary learning has been done *before* he steps aboard a new type of aircraft. Certainly there will be no room for a learning curve in the days of the jumbo jets and supersonic transports.

But in fairness to the carriers and their training procedures, it is essential to examine the Moss findings a little further. They cast an illuminating light on the primary reasons behind jet accidents.

First, it should be remembered that his survey covered all airlines except those behind the Iron Curtain (Russia's state-owned and -operated carrier, Aeroflot, has an unknown safety record because the Soviet Union does not always disclose fatal crashes unless foreigners were among the passengers). Many foreign carriers such as Japan Air Lines, Britain's BOAC, SAS, Swissair, Alitalia, Lufthansa and numerous others have safety performances as good as that of any U.S. airline. But a few do not and Moss was not trying to whitewash the jets; he included *all* crashes.

Bearing this in mind, the Moss study showed some remarkable causal patterns.

For one thing, 20 percent of the crashes were on training flights when pilots were exposed to abnormal situations and operating conditions—such as trying to maneuver at low altitudes with power cut on two out of four engines. The most significant finding was that 63 percent of the crashes occurred during the landing phase, *with 80 percent of these taking place in areas of the world where only 17 percent of the landings are made* "and where the quality of navigational aids and traffic control is the lowest," as Moss emphasized. These areas included Asia, South and Central America, and Africa.

By contrast, North America—with 62 percent of the world's scheduled landings—had only 10 percent of the landing accidents. Europe, which also has superior airport facilities, had 21 percent of the landings and only 10 percent of the landing crashes.

One of the nation's top safety experts, Jerome Lederer of NASA (formerly Director of the Flight Safety Foundation), commented wryly on this correlation between accidents and lack of landing aids by pointing out that "a cost benefit study might show that the installation and operation of these aids would have cost less than the accidents their absence induced."

The Pan Am captain found pilot error involved as a possible contributory cause in 83 percent of the accidents. Weather was cited as a contributing factor in 40 percent, navigational aids 38 percent, maintenance 35 percent, design 35 percent and sabotage 4 percent. Moss, a veteran pilot himself, did not duck the hot-potato issue of crew mistakes. He pointed out that in general, pilot goofs were triggered by factors outside the cockpit such as nav aid malfunctions and weather. But he added:

"In spite of these prior contributory factors, it still remains that the flight crew did not *prevent* [his italics] the accident from happening. I maintain that the prime duty of the flight crew is to cope with the failures of designers, of maintenance, of other humans; this is why our airplanes are not fully automated . . ."

Having tagged pilots with a large measure of responsibility, Captain Moss went on to plead for better tools with which pilots can work. Specifically:

—Improved nav aids in underequipped areas, such as visual glide paths.

—Better cockpit facilities for chart reading at night; Moss believes this outwardly insignificant item is a prime safety matter, with pilots relying on memory for important altitudes because it is too difficult to read and/or so easy to misread charts at night. He declared that improved cockpit lighting would reduce the incidence of hitting mountains on initial descent, hills on initial approaches, or undershoots on final approach—all three frequent repeaters in the circumstances of jet crashes.

—Up-to-date operations manuals as well as adequate "by the book" training. "It is not enough to assume that a man will learn the procedures himself, nor is it enough to assume that he will remember them forever," Moss added.

That latter recommendation will later acquire the luster of perspicacity when we delve more deeply into individual jet crashes, several of which involved training loopholes as a major causal factor. In the training category, Moss offered this frank advice to all airlines: get chief pilots who are not afraid to take disciplinary action and who also are not intimidated by top management.

The Moss survey hit hard at a generally unsuspected and vastly underrated area of concern in the jet age complacency. The dates of occurrence for the 40 fatal accidents he studied show clear evidence that many carriers tend to tighten up procedures and precautions after a bad accident, then after a period of uneventful operations they seem to relax until tragedy strikes again. In effect, Moss was the first responsible airline official who supported that famous "rule of three" superstition—the belief that airline accidents occur in groups of three. Moss indicated it is not a superstition or a coincidence, but a statistical fact stemming from complacency. Explained Moss:

"It is human nature to relax your guard after a certain period. Then lightning strikes. We have a series of accidents in close succession, and we tighten up our procedures operationally and maintenance-wise . . . This accomplishes the objective and we control the accident picture —until we are lulled into a false sense of security again and the stage is set for another rude awakening by a series of accidents."

It should be reiterated again that the Moss study, its conclusions and criticisms, were directed at airlines in general. He found the U.S. jet safety record markedly superior to the overall world rate and he attributed this in part to the fact that the United States never tries to sweep an accident under a rug. Moss noted that the causes of only about half the foreign crashes covered in his report were officially and publicly reported subsequent to the accidents. By contrast, the United States issues full and detailed reports on all crashes and makes them readily available not only in this country but abroad.

It is no coincidence that the U.S. safety record is one of the best in the world, Moss said, "because prompt public disclosure of accident facts and circumstances . . . has had a marked effect on the U.S. record."

In October of 1968, Moss took a fresh look at the entire decade of jet operations and came up with even more favorable figures. There were 70 fatal jet accidents in that period—during a total of more than 28.5 million hours flown. Only a half-dozen airliners were operating jets in the first full year of the jet age. By 1968, carriers flying jets totaled 149.

The safety record "has improved better than fivefold" in the past decade, Moss told the Flight Safety Foundation's annual air safety seminar. "I think we can say, with certainty, that the more we fly the safer we get. The learning curve works."

The Pan Am official said U.S. and many foreign airlines actually have achieved the incredible rate of only one accident for every 2 million hours flown, although he added that "how to extend this excellent record worldwide is the first challenge, while the second challenge is to start the first of the second generation jets high up on the learning curve."

The Moss analysis still was valid despite a rash of bad U.S. crashes in December of 1968 that made the year the second worst in history for total passenger deaths—303 compared to 336 in 1960. There were 4 fatal accidents in that single month, although only one of them involved a jet. Yet even with 1968's comparatively poor record, the statistics added up to 2 fatal crashes for every one million flights—a higher rate than the above, but still far superior to accident rates in the days of the pistons. (5)

An equally interesting approach to safety statistics was made by Robert F. Dressler, a special FAA consultant, in a paper read before the International Air Safety Seminar at Madrid in 1966. Dressler took a different tack than Moss in that he broke down aircraft accidents in terms of three categories—takeoff, cruise, and landing—and weighed the relative safety of all types of planes in each operational phase.

Dressler's survey covered 318 accidents, fatal and nonfatal, involving U.S. carriers between 1961 and 1964. On the basis of this study, he found that:

—Jets were twice as dangerous during takeoff and landing as pistons or propjets.

—The jets' cruise risk decreased 40 percent in the four-year period, to the point where cruise risk was almost negligible compared to the takeoff and landing phases.

—Cruise risk was almost identical for jets, pistons, and propjets alike.

—Pistons were safest in landings and propjets were safest in takeoffs.

—There was a distinct correlation between landing speeds and landing risks, the jets' higher landing speeds being a definite contributory factor in accidents occurring in this phase.

The Dressler statistics seem to cast a jaundiced eye on the jets, but they should not be interpreted as a flat "jets are more dangerous" conclusion. Obviously they are more vulnerable to landing and takeoff accidents because in too many instances they operate at airports designed for piston-engine transports (see Chapter 4). And Dressler's inclusion of *nonfatal* accidents gave him an entirely different statistical base than Moss's.

Examining any set of safety statistics reminds one of the fable about the three blind men who touched an elephant and then described the animal in terms of whatever part of the animal's anatomy each happened to grab. On one hand, we have the august Senate Aeronautical and Space Sciences Committee, which in February of 1967 issued a sharply critical report on air safety.

"Aviation safety shows no signs of improvement," the Committee declared. "Scheduled air safety statistics show that aviation safety has not improved much over the past seventeen years."

The report complained about "year-to-year fluctuations," noting that 1966 was the safest year in U.S. commercial aviation history ("a remarkable improvement," the Committee said) but that 1967 saw a reversion to the fifteen-year average.

On the other hand, it could be argued with admirable logic that keeping the fatality and accident rate consistently low is no minor achievement—considering the technical aspects of the jet revolution. The 1967 statistics would have just about equaled 1966's, as a matter of fact, were it not for two midair collisions between airliners and private planes—both accidents in which the airlines involved could shoulder little or no part of the blame. Just one or two crashes, occurring under circumstances divorced from airline safety practices, can cause havoc to safety statistics. It would be fairer to examine the reasons behind transport crashes before indicting the industry for what appears to be a status quo record. It also must be admitted that even a fluctuating record, if the average rate is low, has to indicate an enormous amount of safety progress. The jet age, with built-in seeds of trouble in the form of more complex planes, swollen passenger lists, and routine operations in weather that once would have caused flight cancellations, could have been disastrous if it were not for dramatic improvements and unappreciated accomplishments. It might be mentioned that the most frequent reasons for jet crashes listed in the Moss study were the same as those which have resulted in fatal accidents to older planes. Comparatively few were analogous to jet operations, which makes the overall performance of the turbine-powered fleet even more remarkable.

Yet it is not a proud past that concerns many in aviation, but a future that by its own expanding nature *cannot* rely on any fluctuating—however slight—or generally static accident rate. Put the record of U.S. aviation's best year—1966—into the year 1970 and you might have a catastrophic situation. In 1966, the nation's scheduled airlines had 3 fatal accidents with a fatality total of only 59 lives. But suppose there were 3 fatal accidents involving jumbo jets or supersonic transports.

The crash of a single Boeing 747 jumbo jet, which can carry between 350 and 450 passengers, could be the statistical equivalent of three DC-8 or 707 accidents. The same will be true of the American SST. The worst annual death toll for U.S. carriers was 307 in 1960. Bobbie Allen, former Director of the Department of Transportation's Safety Board and the nation's top accident investigator, is one who believes a rate decline is mandatory.

"When I look at the projected increase in activity," Allen told an Aviation/Space Writers Association meeting in Washington, "I become apprehensive because accident statistics that are acceptable today may become intolerable tomorrow."

The airlines themselves are apprehensive, too, because they readily agree that air travel must be made even safer. Again, safety and economic progress in the industry have been blood brothers. The industry is well aware of what a single jumbo jet or SST crash can mean, not only in terms of human tragedy and statistics, but also in terms of financial loss. James Fortuna, Vice President of

United States Aviation Underwriters, has estimated that a 350-passenger jet has a loss potential of $55 million just in passenger insurance claims, not to mention the $20 million value of the aircraft itself, plus whatever claims might be filed for damage or injury to persons and property on the ground.

A court awarded the family of a man killed in a 1963 jet crash no less than $2 million. A total of 115 damage suits were filed after the collision of a United DC-8 and TWA Constellation over New York's Staten Island in 1960. The claims amounted to nearly $80 million. Many carriers are considering formation of an airline-owned insurance company before the jumbos and supersonics come along in force.

There have been some startling projections made on the assumption that the airline accident rate will continue to remain relatively static. One authority predicted 140 fatal crashes on the world's scheduled airlines over the next five years, with 1,400 passenger deaths. The gloomiest and most quoted forecast comes from Bo Lundberg, for years head of Sweden's Aeronautical Foundation (and a vitriolic opponent of the SST). Lundberg took the anticipated growth in passenger miles flown, applied the average world accident rate for the past ten years, and arrived at the conclusion that by the year 2000 we can expect 10,000 deaths a year in airliner crashes unless the present rate is reduced drastically—and 1,100 annual fatalities as early as 1975.

Such doleful crystal ball reflections may be statistically possible but are not very likely, if past performance and future plans are considered. There was a veritable voices-of-doom chorus ten years ago when the jets began operating, and now the same voices are being aimed in the direction of the jet revolution's second stage—the jumbos and the supersonics. What follows in this book should provide reassurance that the airlines intend to make that second stage even safer than the first—not only with the newer planes but in operations involving the older jets.

If anyone thinks the public is not conscious of and interested in air safety problems, he might inspect about thirty folders on the seventh floor of the big Federal Aviation Administration building in Washington.

Each folder carries the label: "IDEAS ON AIR SAFETY FROM THE PUBLIC." They include correspondence from learned aeronautical engineers, complete with blueprints. There also are laboriously scrawled, crude drawings from children. One letter is from an inventor outlining his proposal for a new type of airliner seat. There is another from an eleven-year-old boy addressed to the late President John F. Kennedy. It starts out: "I'm sorry to bother you, but I have an idea on how to make airplanes safer."

This was accompanied by a pencil drawing of a crippled airliner, with a huge parachute attached to the fuselage. Actually, the youngster's idea is the most frequent suggestion made to FAA. The agency answers each one with the patient explanation that even if it were possible to design a parachute capable of supporting the weight of a huge jetliner, such a chute would be so heavy by itself that passenger and baggage capacity would have to be limited.

The FAA answers every letter, no matter how farfetched or crackpot it may seem. In some cases, it merely acknowledges the correspondence with a polite note thanking the writer for his interest in air safety. Suggestions which may have some merit are turned over to FAA's Safety and Engineering Division.

The majority of letters seek financial help for further experimentation. A great proportion present ideas or theories which already are the subject of current testing or which have been discarded on the basis of previous experiments. And curiously enough, most of them have come in since 1960.

Quite a few bring smiles to FAA's engineers—like the one which began belligerently: "I think this idea is good. It's better than the ones you have, which are nothing."

Or the writer who simply informed FAA: "I have a device which will prevent all crashes. Please reply soon."

Many safety proposals are ingenious, if impractical. Samples:

—Build a conveyor belt at airports, the belt moving at the same speed as a landing aircraft so a plane making a wheels-up landing would merely have to set down on the belt. (Wheels-up landings are not a serious problem, seldom result in anything but minor damage, and the belt idea would be too expensive.)

—Put a big cradle on a flatcar which would move down the runway and catch a crippled airliner as it settled down. (Same objections.)

—Equip each airliner with a telescopic tube, through which passengers could be transferred from a crippled plane to another aircraft while still in flight. (Such a tube would have to be at least 75 feet long to keep the planes safely separated, and strong enough to allow the passage of persons at about 150 miles an hour—all of which adds up to a device so heavy that no transport plane could carry one.)

—Install a loud siren on every plane so the pilot could warn people on the ground if his aircraft was about to crash. (No comment necessary.)

—Put a long steel rod in the nose of every plane, with a steel spring attached to absorb the shock if the aircraft struck a mountain. (No comment necessary.)

—Line airliner cabins with asbestos so that temperatures from post-impact fire could be kept low while passengers were evacuating. (To keep temperatures below 150° F for a five-minute evacuation would require asbestos about two inches thick—thus adding around 9,000 pounds of weight to the airframe. Actually, new cabin-lining materials have been perfected for present and future airliners which provide thermal protection with no weight penalty; they are described in a subsequent chapter.)

—Have every airliner equipped with a capsule that could be ejected automatically on impact. It would contain any last messages from the crew, comments from the passengers, and even such valuables as jewelry and wallets. (Pilots are too busy in an emergency to start writing notes for capsules. Anyway, new cockpit voice recorders are required for all jets and would fill much the same purpose. Also being considered is a crash locator beacon, ejected automatically and capable of sending radio signals that would guide rescue parties to the scene of a remote crash.)

—Planes should be able to fire rockets ahead of them into areas of suspected turbulence. If the rocket is caught in rough air, it could send a warning signal back to the plane. (Major research is being conducted on means to detect clear-air turbulence, largely through "sensors" which operate on a heat principle because turbulence is associated with temperature changes. This work will be described more fully in another chapter.)

Next to parachutes for planes, the most frequent suggestion submitted to FAA involves a means of jettisoning the wings if a crash were inevitable. FAA concedes the theory is admirable because this would eliminate a fire danger. But the fuel system of a modern plane is intricate, with complex plumbing and pumping lines throughout the fuselage and wings. Any wing-jettison device would have to disconnect automatically the entire fuel system. Engineers are wary of any gimmick subject to inadvertent activation, thus creating an even worse danger than the one it is supposed to eliminate.

The truth is that the FAA has yet to get an idea from the public which would warrant further investigation—with one exception. A youngster sent in a plan for an airliner seat with crash-resistant qualities. It was good enough to intrigue FAA technicians. But when they looked into it further, they discovered that a similar seat already had been designed and found to be too complicated and heavy.

At least the public is well-meaning and interested in what is being done and what will be done to make flying safer. Yet whatever gadgets, devices, and hardware are developed, air safety still depends to a great extent on the skill, training, and dedication of the men in the cockpit.

3. "IT'S WHAT'S UP FRONT THAT COUNTS"

Kimes . . . White . . . Carroll . . . Duescher. . . .

Ask any airline passenger if those names mean anything, and the odds are about 100 million to one against any of them being recognized. That isn't surprising but in a way it is too bad. Those four names were responsible for preserving the lives of 318 fellow human beings.

Kimes . . . White . . . Carroll . . . Duescher . . . Each wore the four stripes of an airline captain, four tiny bands of gold or silver on the sleeves of their uniform coats—those four bands that mean the culmination of years of training and an unspoken but sacred sense of responsibility.

Each was "fully qualified to serve as airline captain, having completed the required qualifications for the high responsibilities and public trust of the position," as "the captain's diploma" for one major airline puts it. Individually, they worked for four different airlines—Pan American, Eastern, Trans World and United. But their braided caps could have carried the insignia of any airline. They were typical of their profession, products of the world's finest flight training, and possessing the three qualities that comprise the character of the airline pilot—skill, courage, and coolness under pressure.

These are their stories. They are not told to glorify the four men but rather to present them as airline captains whose professional performances could have been duplicated by thousands of their fellow pilots. This is not to disparage what they did, but merely to point out that they saved 318 lives primarily because they came out of an industry training system specifically designed to deal with emergencies. Undoubtedly they *did* perform "above and beyond" normal airmanship. But basically that is what an airline pilot is trained for and what he is paid for—the ability to analyze an abnormal situation instantly and react correctly. Anyone who questions the validity of paying airline pilots up to $59,000 a year should realize that a captain flying a $6 million airplane crammed with trusting passengers can earn the $59,000 in a few seconds. Like Charles H. Kimes.

There were 143 passengers plus a crew of 10 aboard Pan American World Airways Flight 843 when it took off from San Francisco for Honolulu on June 28, 1965.

First Officer Fred R. Miller was at the controls as the Boeing 707 screamed down the runway, a 270,000-pound defiance of gravity.

"Eighty knots," Captain Kimes called out. "Ninety. One hundred."

The nosewheel pounded and thumped. The four engines were spewing at least 95 percent of full-rated power.

"V_1," Kimes announced—the takeoff point of no return.

"Rotate!" Kimes's order was followed instantly by Miller's applying gentle back pressure on the yoke. The 707's nose lifted. The main-landing-gear wheels left the ground with a thud that was almost a protest.

"V_2," Kimes said. This was minimum safe airspeed. Flight 843 climbed smoothly, its great bulk and immense power providing the peculiar sensory illusion that is part of the jet age—the feeling that the aircraft is hooked to a giant railroad track curving into the sky. The four men in the cockpit began to relax almost imperceptibly, the inevitable tenseness of every takeoff disappearing magically with the sound of "V_2" and the moment of miracle that is flight itself.

In the cabin, Mr. and Mrs. Louis Swanson and their two sons—Louis, eleven, and Joseph, seven—settled back in their seats. The Swansons were from McAdoo, Pennsylvania, and had been attending a Lions Club International convention in Los Angeles. They had never been to Hawaii and after the convention they had flown to San Francisco for connections with Pan Am 843.

Young Louis had a window seat just over the right

wing. His brother wanted to know if the plane was "up in the air yet."

"Just about," Louis said with the half-bored, patronizing air of an eleven-year-old talking to a seven-year-old. He still was looking out the window at the wing when he froze.

"Mommy, Mommy!" he shouted. "The wing's on fire! Look!"

Mrs. Swanson peered out too. Flames were gushing from the outboard engine. "It's all over for us," she thought dully.

Jorge Rivera, a chemistry student from Hawaii, had felt the thud of the retracting landing gear as it was tucked away into the belly wheel well. But not more than ninety seconds later, he felt another jolt of a different intensity and source. He looked up and saw a faint, glowlike reflection in the cabin. Almost automatically, he glanced outside. The engine farthest away from him was gone and the wing was on fire.

Mrs. Kaleo Schroder, a California schoolteacher traveling with her three children, saw the engine leave the wing. The flames seemed to crawl directly toward them. The children began crying. Mrs. Schroder tried to calm them. Her own reaction was curiously unperturbed. The night before, she had dreamed that something was going to happen to the plane and her first reaction was, "Well, it's happening."

Unperturbed was not the word for passenger Minoru Fujioka of Hawaii. He and his wife had just bid goodbye to their eighteen-year-old son, who was enrolling in the Air Force Academy at Colorado Springs. Fujioka was not a religious man. But when he saw the fire sweep the outer portion of the wing, he prayed. Mrs. Fujioka thought only of her son.

"He will never see me again," she said to herself.

In the cockpit, Kimes and his three colleagues felt the 707 shudder violently. A red light just above the instrument panel flashed angrily and a loud bell sounded. It was a fire warning from the number four engine. Kimes could not know it, but a turbine wheel had disintegrated, flying apart with a force that amounted to an internal explosion. Those compressor wheels whirl 10,000 times a minute, impelled by combustion that has been measured at 1600° F —a gigantic blowtorch capable of melting lead or aluminum. The disintegration of the compressor wheel sent steel slivers throughout the engine, smashing the combustion chamber. The "blowtorch" was set free, its unchained heat roaring out of the shattered engine and licking a searing path to the wing.

Kimes, sitting in the traditional left seat of an aircraft commander, could not see what was happening to the fire-threatened right wing. For that matter, neither could co-pilot Miller, because of the 707's sharp wing sweepback. He saw the fire but did not see the engine fall off and reported to Kimes that the outer starboard wing tank must have exploded. Kimes, acting instinctively, took over the controls. This was no slur on Miller's ability: when an airliner gets into serious trouble, most captains will assume command.

When the engine fell off the burning wing, the jet lurched sharply to the right. Kimes glanced quickly at his altimeter. They were at 700 feet, nose high about 15 degrees. He decided to keep climbing; the higher the altitude, the easier it would be to maneuver. Flying a jet at low altitude can be the equivalent of flying an iron bathtub. Even as he tried to digest the emergency, he thought of his passengers. He clicked on the cabin PA mike.

"Folks, we have a little minor problem," he started off calmly.

Miller looked at him quizzically.

"Well, maybe it's not so minor," Kimes added in a voice so nonchalant that he might have been delivering a "glad to have you with us today" welcome.

The shuddering had stopped but the 707 was handling like a car with its front wheels completely out of alignment. Thanks to the fire and the shock of the number four engine pod being torn off, approximately 25 feet of the right wing was gone and Kimes literally was flying a 707 with not much more than a wing and a half.

He increased power on the remaining three engines, delicately manipulating the two port throttles and coordinating his rudder controls to counter the plane's skidding tendency. He also had enough of a sense of responsibility toward his passengers to realize that they must be terrified and probably on the verge of panic. As busy as he was, he managed to speak over the PA again.

"We've had some trouble," he told them—still in a tone bordering on the placid. "Please put on your life jackets.

There is no danger whatsoever. Just keep calm and everything will be okay."

The troubles of Flight 843 by this time had attracted the attention of thousands on the ground, including Lieutenant Melvin Hartman of the United States Coast Guard. Hartman immediately took off in a Coast Guard amphibian plane and flew close to the stricken 707. To the young pilot, the Boeing "looked like a big Roman candle." Kimes was later to express fervent gratitude for Hartman's alertness and decision to "ride shotgun" on the staggering jet. The Pan Am captain sent two Mayday messages to the San Francisco control tower, but these traditional distress signals went unheard—Flight 843's radios were acting up and the transmissions were too weak for the traffic controllers to hear the calls.

Hartman heard them, however, and acted as a communications relay between the crippled jetliner and the San Francisco tower. Actually, controllers already were aware that 843 was in trouble. One minute after the plane took off, the tower saw the flames erupt from number four engine and advised all flights:

"Stand by. Emergency in progress."

Kimes decided to level off at about 1,300 feet. He would have preferred going higher but by this time he was uncertain whether the battered right wing would hold. He continued to nurse throttles and controls, while almost simultaneously making sure that his passengers were briefed on what was now an inevitable emergency landing. Kimes does not recall specifically what he said on the PA, but Mrs. Ruby Leonard—a registered nurse with the Idaho Department of Health—took the trouble to write Pan Am later about what went on in the cabin where she and her 141 fellow passengers wondered how close they were to death.

". . . the captain's voice came over the intercom and in a very reassuring manner he told us that if we would obey orders there was no need to panic; that everyone should put on his life jacket; take off his shoes; place his pillow on his lap; and lean forward . . . He also told us to remove any sharp obstacles [she meant objects] and wrap our hands around our ankles. He appealed to us as adults and told us that he expected us to handle our emotional reactions in a mature way. When he had given us these instructions and everyone was madly scrambling to follow his instructions, the panic was reduced immeasurably . . ."

Although painfully unsure of the integrity of the damaged wing, Kimes decided not to attempt a landing at San Francisco International Airport. He headed instead for Travis Air Force Base 50 miles away, cognizant of its longer runways and superb emergency and rescue facilities. It took guts to make that decision, for he was battling a very natural instinct to get down on the ground as quickly as possible. The cabin was quiet; the six flight attendants— the purser and five stewardesses—had everything under control and ready for landing.

Flight 843's takeoff had been logged at 2:10 P.M. PDT. It was shortly before 2:30 that Kimes began circling Travis, with fighter planes hovering around protectingly and Hartman's amphibian lumbering along behind. Now a new crisis arose. When Kimes told Miller to lower the landing gear, nothing happened. There had been an apparent hydraulic failure, and there was no time to fool with the primary system. Miller, Second Officer Max Webb, and Flight Engineer Fitch Robertson opened a floor hatch and cranked the gear down manually.

Flight 843 landed smoothly and safely at 2:30 P.M. Only nineteen minutes had elapsed between the engine explosion and touchdown at Travis. Many of the passengers wept as they disembarked, tears of gratitude as well as nervous reaction. Unfortunately, they were due for a new shock.

Pan Am ferried another plane to Travis to fly them back to San Francisco. As it landed at the Air Force base, the nosewheel collapsed. There were no injuries to the embarrassed crew, but some of the passengers could have been forgiven if they had abandoned air travel permanently.

Finally, they boarded a third jet, which returned them to San Francisco International Airport. En route, Captain Kimes apologized over the PA for what had happened to the original ferry plane as well as Flight 843. The passengers laughed and applauded him. Five hours after their original departure, they left for Hawaii in a fourth jet— slightly numb from the drinks Pan Am had served them at the airport, plus a sumptuous dinner. Many were later to write either Kimes or the airline, expressing gratitude for his skill and the actions of the entire crew.

There were other aftermaths for Kimes too. He received some 500 letters of congratulations, including one from Vice President Humphrey. An Ohio minister whose young daughter was on Flight 843 wrote a particularly touching note which said, "I believe that you had one passenger aboard who occupied no seat but was present with each passenger and crew member."

With that, Captain Charles H. Kimes was in full agreement.

The forty-four-year-old native of Enid, Oklahoma, answered every letter personally, with some secretarial aid from Pan Am. The response to his handling of the emergency—FAA Administrator Najeeb E. Halaby called it "a masterful feat of airmanship" when he gave Kimes a special citation—was embarrassing, for the Captain is a modest man. One firm sent him a $500 check. Kimes acknowledged it with a letter in which he reminded the donor:

". . . under any normal emergency I could quite easily pocket your largess and have a ball . . . But in the situation you write about I'd have been treading water in a lead life jacket without the entire cooperation of all my crew and passengers. I do not say this in false modesty . . . but panic could easily have resulted had not my flight service crew busied themselves and kept passengers busy with the donning of life jackets, emergency instructions, etc."

Kimes split the $500 into ten checks of $50 each and gave one to each of his crew. When a television manufacturer sent him two TV sets, the captain insisted on the entire crew drawing straws—and was secretly happy when he lost. At a news conference shortly after the incident, Kimes remarked to the reporters that "There has been misunderstanding of my role. I was just one of ten crew members," he added. "I did nothing outstanding. I don't feel I should wear a hero's hat. If any acknowledgment at all is in order, it should go to the training department of Pan American."

The training department deserved credit, but so did Captain Kimes and the rest of the crew. Kimes and his three flight deck colleagues collectively were given the 1965 Daedalian Award, presented annually to an airline pilot who has demonstrated outstanding skill in handling an emergency. At least a dozen major newspapers printed laudatory editorials, all stressing the theme that what Kimes performed was a service to aviation and the professional reputation of the airline pilot. But perhaps the warmest praise of all came from Boeing.

The manufacturer's engineers admitted they never dreamed it was aerodynamically possible to keep a 707 in the air with one third of a wing gone.

"We run just about every kind of test imaginable," said one Boeing technician, "but you never imagine a plane in this kind of a situation remaining flyable. That cockpit was full of real pros."

In a very real sense, the story of Flight 843 was a tribute to Boeing, too, for it demonstrated the importance of all U.S. transport manufacturers' "fail-safe" philosophy—a design concept insisting that the structural failure of any single component must not be allowed to progress to other parts. On a plane not designed under this rule, the loss of a huge wing section would be fatal because the remaining structure would be incapable of absorbing the additional load.

Less than six months later, the value of "fail-safe" was to be demonstrated again, once more in a Boeing 707 but also in the hearts and minds of two airline captains whose fates and planes alike were on a collision course in the skies over the small town of Carmel, New York.

The date was December 4, 1965, and the time was 4:19 P.M. EST.

At that precise moment, a TWA 707 and an Eastern Constellation collided at 11,000 feet. The impact tore off 30 feet of the jet's left wing and severed the entire control system of the piston-engine "Connie"—rudder and elevator boost package, control cables for elevators and ailerons, and even the trim tab cables.

By every logical assumption and law of aerodynamics, both planes and the 109 human beings aboard them were doomed. One wing of the jet was less than two-thirds intact—worse damage than on the Pan Am 707—and there also was fire. The Constellation was in even worse shape, the equivalent of an automobile whose steering column has been snapped in two.

The TWA 707 was Flight 42, San Francisco to Kennedy International Airport. Commanding was Captain Thomas H. Carroll, forty-five. The flight was about 40 miles from a navigation checkpoint at Carmel when Air Traffic Control instructed it to descend to 11,000 feet. TWA 42 reported at that altitude one minute before the collision.

Carroll had flicked on the FASTEN SEAT BELTS sign, anticipating some turbulence as they approached New York. When the collision impact occurred, there was a sharp jolt, but many passengers thought they merely had encountered rough air—until those on the left side saw part of the wing gone and fire break out. One of these horrified passengers was an electronics expert who was in the process of reading a technical report on air safety. It included methods of preventing midair collisions.

Five passengers seated on the left side saw the Constellation just before the aircraft paths bisected. One was John Hollingsworth of Westport, Connecticut, who felt the jolt and then heard the incongruous sound of breaking glass (which came, he learned later, from the galley). Only one terrible conclusion went through his mind: "This is it."

That was close to what Captain Carroll was thinking, too, but as more of a fleeting subconscious thought. An airline pilot has no time for such luxuries as meditation when an emergency strikes. Carroll had the 707 on autopilot, but his left hand was on the control yoke when he saw a blue and white aircraft at 10 o'clock high. Carroll's reaction was lightning-quick. He disengaged the autopilot with his left thumb, put the control yoke wheel hard over to the right, and almost in the same motion pulled back on the yoke. Copilot Leo Smith grabbed the controls simultaneously.

The 707 rolled like a frightened whale trying to escape a killer shark. But Carroll quickly realized that the maneuver would not take them out of collision course. Both pilots reversed the control forces, with a hard-over wheel turn to the left and a push forward on the yoke. The 707 had barely begun to respond when the two planes hit. The first maneuver, a sharp, climbing turn, was intended to take them over the Constellation. The second was an attempt to dive under it when Carroll became aware that the smaller plane was climbing faster than the jet in its own avoidance maneuver.

Carroll fought to get the 707 back to even keel. Smith spoke twelve terse words into his radio microphone, tuned to the frequency of New York Air Route Traffic Control Center.

"Just had midair collision with blue Constellation. Request expeditious approach to Kennedy."

The stunned Center gave the jet immediate priority, clearing all traffic below 11,000 feet and giving Flight 42 a straight-in path to Kennedy. But Carroll had more problems than just a fast clearance. The 707 was reeling. Carroll, Smith, and Flight Engineer Ernest Hall assessed the damage and Smith notified Kennedy to have crash and fire equipment standing by. The wing fire had dwindled to mere smoke but the crew was taking no chances.

As Captain Kimes had acted six months before, so did Carroll—carrying the double burden of maintaining control and stifling the almost inevitable panic that must be poisoning the cabin. Actually, his passengers were too frightened to show panic. The shock of the collision—the crew felt two jolts but some passengers were aware of only one—sent handbags, coats, briefcases, and other carry-on items flying through the cabin. For as long as fifteen seconds, the 707 bounced up and down.

"It was like a hurricane," one passenger recalled later. "I heard the pilot make an announcement but I don't remember what he said. I was too scared."

What Carroll was delivering was the usual "planned emergency" instruction list—loosen ties, take sharp objects out of pockets, women remove high-heel shoes, and everybody stay calm while following the orders of the hostesses. He did not mention that a collision had occurred—just that an emergency landing was necessary. Flight 42 swept toward Kennedy, a semblance of stability restored. Carroll flew a 360-degree turn to the left over the airport while men in the control tower checked to see if the landing gear was down—Carroll didn't trust the green "down and locked" lights in front of him, and he had indications that at least some hydraulic pressure had been lost.

TWA 42 landed at 4:40 P.M., nineteen minutes after the collision, with Carroll having to resort to reverse thrust alone after he discovered he had no wheel brakes working. When the jet finally came to a stop, about ten passengers emerged via the main door emergency slide. TWA officials interrupted the evacuation when they saw no sign of fire and the remainder of the passengers left in normal fashion. There was only one injury—a hostess knocked off her feet by the collision impact had suffered a bloody nose.

One of the first questions asked by Carroll and his crew was about the fate of the other plane. The TWA captain was to find out later that his own emergency, brilliantly handled as it was, amounted to relative routine compared with the ordeal of Eastern 853 and a captain named Charles J. White.

White was the son of a New York City detective, born and raised in Brooklyn. At the age of nineteen, Charlie White was one of the youngest bomber captains in the Air Force during World War II. In 1948, he voluntarily left his job at Eastern to fly the Berlin airlift and he earned a college degree by going to night school while flying for the airline—two indications of his determination and his sense of duty.

White was to display both qualities again on this day of December 4, plus raw courage. He was commanding Eastern Flight 853, one of the airline's popular "shuttle" trips from Boston to Newark. He had 49 passengers aboard—a light load for the shuttle, but this was a Saturday afternoon and air traffic is fairly light on most Saturdays.

They were at 10,000 feet, the nose of their Constellation poking in and out of whipped cream puffs of clouds that occasionally blossomed above a fairly thick cloud deck. Most pilots love this particular phase of flight—skimming along on top of a cloud bank which provides the rare sensation of speed and motion.

The old Connie, one of the most beautiful airplanes ever built with its sharklike fuselage and triple tail, was just emerging from a cloud when copilot Roger Holt saw an object at two o'clock—a heart-freezing sight that caused him almost to shriek a warning to White. Seemingly at their own altitude and on a converging course was a red and white jetliner.

"Look out!" Holt yelled.

Both pilots, as though their arms were hooked to a single brain, pulled back on their yokes. But in virtually the same second the jet began climbing too.

The jet's left wing sliced into the Constellation's tail, severing one third of the structure and leaving control cables dangling like ganglia from a disemboweled animal. Eastern 853 was moving at 240 miles an hour and the TWA jet was doing nearly 400. Yet while the impact shock was violent on the big jet, the crew and passengers on EAL 853 felt only a curiously gentle bump, hardly any stronger than a bit of minor turbulence. The mildness was deceiving; the Constellation was mortally hurt.

The Eastern plane continued climbing momentarily after the collision. White pushed forward on his yoke. There was no response. The Constellation shuddered and stalled. The nose came down and the plane began to dive. White cut the power just as Flight Engineer Emile Greenway gulped nervously at what his panel was showing. Four red lights flashed multiple warnings—hydraulic pressure was dropping to zero.

"Pressure and quantity!" Greenway yelled. "Pressure and quantity!"

He was telling the captain they had lost their hydraulic boost package—the equivalent of power steering on a car. White pulled a lever that normally would have shifted the controls from hydraulic to manual, thus allowing him to move his elevators, ailerons, and rudders by applying a lot of muscle. This time White needed prayer, not muscle. The mechanical linkage had snapped as well as the hydraulic lines. There was no control. The nose-heavy Constellation dove headlong toward inevitable disaster, picking up speed even with the engines throttled down.

"Power!" copilot Holt yelled. "How about the power?"

White nodded. He pushed all four throttles forward. Power was all he had. He knew it would increase the speed of the dive but it was the only way to bring the nose up—the higher speed and faster revolutions of the props would create more lift under the wings.

The plane plunged through the cloud layer, engines roaring. The Constellation trembled as the nose came up with agonizing slowness. Level. Then a nose-up attitude again, a climb that would result inevitably in a second stall. But White was improvising now, manipulating his throttles like a piano virtuoso expertly fingering his keys. With incredible swiftness, he mastered the throttle combination that gave him enough power to keep the nose reasonably level.

The Constellation was in a steady left turn. White found he could straighten out to some extent by carefully nursing the throttle settings—full power on number one, slightly less on number two, even less on number three, and further reduction on number four. The engines on a four-engine plane are numbered from left to right. What White did was to create a drastic speed differential between the engines on the left wing and those on the right wing, with the greatest differential between one and four—the outboards. This tended to raise the left wing and gave White some measure of lateral control.

He found time now to talk to his passengers.

"This is the captain speaking."

His voice was calm, with not the slightest hint of fear and impending disaster.

"We've had a midair collision. Please fasten your seat belts."

He paused, the only moment of indecision he was to display. How much could he tell them without causing panic? How do you sugarcoat an announcement of possible, perhaps certain death?

"We're out of control," he said finally—still in a matter-of-fact tone. "Brace yourselves the best you can for a crash landing. You won't be hearing from me any more. I'm going to be a little busy up here."

Only one passenger reacted audibly. A woman wailed briefly. Somebody else snapped, "Shut up, lady!" She subsided. The cabin, except for the two stewardesses moving quickly and efficiently with emergency evacuation preparations, was quiet, in a foglike kind of fear.

Flight Engineer Greenway, meanwhile, had raised the New York Center, which had been trying in vain to contact 853. His message came through loud and clear over the usual filtered, metallic static of air–ground communications.

"Mayday!" he called, repeating the word twice more. "This is Eastern eight fifty-three . . . we've had a midair collision . . . in trouble . . . we're out of control . . ."

He sent the message while the plane still was diving. A few minutes later, after White's masterful use of the throttles, Greenway came back on the radio to ask for a quick routing to Kennedy—he assumed White would want to land where the runways were longest. The Center, which had ordered all aircraft not to interrupt on the frequency 853 was using, gave Greenway clearance to Kennedy. The captain broke in at this point to advise ATC they couldn't make Kennedy or any other airport. The Constellation was descending steadily and there was nothing the crew could do about it. The power settings that kept the aircraft from diving or climbing were insufficient to maintain altitude. White so advised the Center.

"We'll just do the best we can," he added quietly. "Keep an eye on us, please, and see where we're gonna wind up."

White and Holt studied the terrain below. Directly ahead was a fairly large hill covered with trees. Off to the right was a lake and White asked his copilot what he thought about a ditching. Presumably there would be less danger of fire. Holt shook his head; impact with water can be more severe than hitting the ground unless the ditching is perfectly timed. Furthermore, the passengers would not have more than a couple of minutes' survival time in the cold water even if they came through the ditching.

The two pilots looked to the left and saw a grassy pasture on the side of a small hill. It was the only clear area in sight.

"How about that field?" White asked unnecessarily; he had no other choice.

"Let's do it," was Holt's response.

It was getting dark as the Constellation settled toward the field. Behind the airliner was a small private plane occupied by an instructor and student pilot. They had been following the Eastern plane, knowing they were helpless to assist but unwilling to abandon it. The Connie neared the hill and the men in the small plane saw its red anti-collision light suddenly blink off; Greenway had cut off all electrical circuits.

Flight 853's last maneuver could have been classed not only as difficult but almost impossible. White had to bring up the nose just enough to pancake into the slope of the hill. It required split-second timing. If he applied power too soon, the plane would skip over the hill and stall. If he advanced the throttles too late, he would strike the hill in a level nose-first attitude which had to result in a hard, almost certainly fatal impact.

He fingered the cabin PA mike and pressed the transmitting button.

"Brace yourselves," he said. "Here it comes."

White's coordination was perfect but he had some unknown cards stacked against him. In the gathering darkness and from the altitude at which he committed the plane to its last landing, neither he nor Holt could see that the hill was not as clear as they supposed. The Constellation's belly touched the ground with amazing gentleness and the plane skidded up the slope. But just as the crew figured they might have it made, the left wing struck a small tree and tore off. The fuselage and right wing swerved against the far bank of a gully, bounced into the air and struck the ground again. The fuel tanks in the right wing cracked open and a ball of yellow flame billowed a hundred feet into the blackening sky.

By the time the Connie stopped rolling up the hill, its fuselage had split in three places—damage that miraculously saved lives because it provided three additional exits. Passengers, some of them badly hurt, tumbled out of the broken fuselage. Copilot Holt was so seriously injured that he collapsed right after he crawled through or fell out of a cockpit emergency exit. Greenway to this day does not know how he got out and, in fact, does not remember anything that occurred after sending his Mayday message —a frequent traumatic reaction of airmen involved in crashes. Neither the copilot nor flight engineer remembers what happened to White, although they believe the captain may have helped them out of the wreckage.

Only one thing was certain: Charles White never left his plane. His body was found later, not in the cockpit but in the cabin aisle not far from a seat occupied by a dead soldier—the only passenger who failed to get out. Two died later from injuries. It was obvious that the captain went back to the cabin to make sure all his passengers had been evacuated—a final devotion to duty that cost him his life.

Eastern established a college scholarship in his name. He received, posthumously, the 1966 Daedalian Award along with Holt and Greenway. He was buried with full military honors in Arlington National Cemetery and a large plaque honoring his memory hangs in the Eastern terminal building at Kennedy Airport.

On December 20, 1966, more than a year after the collision, the Civil Aeronautics Board issued a report which found an optical illusion responsible for the mishap. The CAB said the cloud bank just under the Constellation in reality sloped downward, giving White and Holt a false horizon. They actually were separated horizontally from the jet by the required 1,000 feet—Eastern had been assigned to 10,000 feet and TWA to 11,000—but were fooled into thinking that TWA was at their altitude. Likewise, the TWA pilots also took evasion action because of an identical illusion—they assumed EAL 853 was at 11,-000. The supreme irony was that the alertness of both crews triggered the collision. It would not have occurred if one or both had not spotted the other.

For Flight Engineer Greenway, the CAB report carried a personal and tragic irony. Ten months before the collision, an Eastern stewardess he had been dating seriously was killed in the crash of a DC-7. The Board's "probable cause" verdict was that the pilots took violent evasive action to avoid what they thought was a collision course with a jet—*because of an optical illusion*—and lost control.

United Air Lines Flight 746, San Francisco–Chicago, was a Boeing 720—in reality just a scaled-down version of the 707, six feet shorter and somewhat lighter in weight.

On July 12, 1963, the lives of 53 passengers aboard Flight 746 were in the hands of a captain named Lynden Duescher. He was only forty-two years old but his logbook showed more than 17,000 hours in the air. He had been a captain since 1945 and, like many pilots, seemed to reflect the character of his airline—cautious, businesslike, quietly efficient.

There are many in aviation who swear different airlines have different personalities, as if they were human instead of corporate, with their crews in some mysterious fashion acquiring the same qualities. TWA, for example, is said to run to the glamorous side and its pilots are frequently of the "Greek god" variety—some airmen claim this is due to the influence of Howard Hughes, who used to own TWA. Eastern's pilots for years had a reputation for resourcefulness and opportunism, which pretty well described Eddie Rickenbacker and his close-to-the-vest policies of running an airline. American has always catered to the business traveler, and not a few of its pilots look as if they had just stepped out of a brokerage office.

This probably explains why so many pilots of other airlines regard United crews with a certain amount of prejudice—the kind of resentful disdain mixed with envy that a younger brother might display toward a somewhat stuffy, better-heeled, and more dignified older kinsman. Actually UAL crews are cast in the same mold as the majority of airmen, but it is hard to convince their competing brethren of this. Because United is the largest U.S. carrier, and one that packs considerable authority in the industry, so do UAL pilots wield hefty influence in the Air Line Pilots Association. Again, its flight crews have assumed a single image reflecting the dominance of their airline—not necessarily an accurate image but one that exists nevertheless. Undoubtedly apocryphal but apt is the story of a flight that was trying frantically to report an emergency simultaneously with a United plane asking for a routine altitude change. The air traffic controller supposedly fielded the competing messages in accordance with protocol.

"Hold up on your Mayday," he advised. "Go ahead United."

At any rate, Lynden Duescher seemed indeed to reflect the businesslike character of his company.

Duescher, in effect, *was* United. Quiet, stolid, not much for fancy or flowery PA announcements, and decidedly professional. It was typical that when United absorbed Capital in 1960, UAL pilots like Duescher referred to their new flight deck brethren as "Brand X." Capital was known as a pilots' airline and mirrored the informality of its crews. United, in turn, was rather formal, far more dignified and markedly conservative by comparison. Which described Lyn Duescher—a firm believer in the airline pilot's creed: "In God we trust; everything else we check."

Before leaving San Francisco, Duescher had examined a company weather forecast indicating an atmospheric disturbance building up over Nebraska. Flight 746 was miles away from the suspected area when the captain turned on his weather-warning radar—with traditional, inherent cautiousness, he wanted plenty of advance notice if the flight was going to encounter turbulence.

The Boeing was at 35,000 feet approaching O'Neill, Nebraska, when its radar picked up mild thunderstorm turbulence ahead. Duescher turned on the seat belt sign and told his crew to fasten their shoulder harnesses. The 720 started to buck.

"Let's see if we can climb above it," Duescher said to copilot Eric Anderson. "Ask ATC for forty-one thousand feet."

Permission to climb to the new altitude was granted. Anderson, who was flying the aircraft, eased back on the yoke. One hundred and thirty-six feet behind the cockpit, the massive elevators hinged to the horizontal tail stabilizers moved slowly and Flight 746 began to climb.

The airspeed increased slowly and the turbulence became slightly choppier. Anderson disengaged the autopilot and assumed manual control. The captain told him to reduce airspeed to the standard maximum for penetrating rough air—250 knots. Flight 746 entered an overcast and bucked even harder. Airspeed and altitude started to fluctuate as alternate updrafts and downdrafts punched at the big jet.

One particularly bad updraft tossed the Boeing 2,000 feet up, and only ten seconds later an equally severe downdraft shoved it down 2,000 feet. Then came another updraft. Flight 746 soared from 37,000 feet to nearly 40,000 in less than ten seconds. The airspeed hovered around 225 knots, dangerously close to a stall at this thin-air altitude.

Both Duescher and Anderson applied forward pressure on the control column and increased power to all four engines, trying to maintain both altitude and airspeed. Turbulence increased and the airspeed indicator was dancing wildly. Now came the first buffeting of a stall. Duescher told his copilot to forget altitude and just concentrate on keeping the nose level and airspeed up. But the nose continued to edge higher. Ten degrees. Fifteen degrees.

The control column was full forward.

The nose crept higher. Twenty degrees. Thirty. Forty. Turbulence shook the plane. Again, the shudder of an impending stall.

Without warning, the bottom dropped out of the sky. A sudden downdraft sucked greedily at 100 tons of metal— an airliner already trimmed for maximum combat against updraft.

Flight 746 fell off on one wing and plummeted out of control toward the ground 40,000 feet below.

Negative G forces clamped their stranglehold on flight deck and cabin alike. Loose articles in the cockpit began floating in the air, then on the ceiling, and finally near the floor. A checklist card drifted aimlessly about, settling eventually on the instrument panel and covering several dials.

In the cabin, objects from the overhead racks launched themselves toward the ceiling. The contents of the rear galley came floating into the cabin. Carry-on luggage leaped from the racks and sailed back toward the rear. A stewardess about to serve a cup of coffee unceremoniously dumped the contents on the floor rug before the hot liquid could jump into a passenger's lap.

There was one passenger who had ignored the FASTEN SEAT BELTS sign, an omission that had remained unspotted by the stewardess. He rose out of his seat all the way to the overhead rack, then descended almost gently to the floor in a prone position. He got back in his seat and this time fastened his belt securely.

Flight 746 was still in the overcast. The nose was pitched down at an attitude of 35 degrees. Airspeed increased ominously. Duescher sent the Air Traffic Control Center in Denver, which was working the flight, a chilling two-word message:

"Aircraft uncontrollable."

Airspeed continued to rise. Duescher chopped his throttles and then pulled the speed brake handle.

Indicated airspeed soared to more than 400 knots. The Mach warning bell clanged. Altimeters spun crazily. Neither the captain nor copilot could read the instruments—still in the overcast, they could have been upside down for all they knew.

Altitude 26,000. Airspeed 480 knots. The Mach warning bell clanged incessantly.

Flight 746 broke out of the overcast, still plunging earthward.

At this moment, it was Duescher's skill and experience plus the structural integrity of a man-made machine pitted against impending disaster. Everything hinged on a tug-of-war between a pilot's instinctive reaction and the training drummed into the mind and soul of every man who flies a jetliner—*"you fly by the book, not by instinct."*

Instinct told him to bring the nose up to check the dive. Instinct told him to do something, anything, to diminish that airspeed.

He had to fight the most immediate and natural temptation—to yank back on the yoke, which would have been either useless or fatal; the Boeing was accelerating too fast. Back pressure sufficient to move the control column would have required superhuman strength on the part of both pilots, and even if they had been able to activate the elevators, a pull-up at this terrific speed probably would have caused structural failure.

He momentarily considered lowering the landing gear, which would have increased drag and maybe induced pitch-up. Panic was battling training. Training won. Lowering the gear might have produced enough drag to tear the plane apart.

He reached for the inboard wing spoiler switch—again, this would have increased drag. But it also might have torn off the wings. Once again, training overrode panic.

Now he tried trimming the stabilizers electrically, but there was no elevator control at sonic speeds.

Altitude 20,000.

Nineteen. Eighteen. Seventeen. Sixteen.

Flight 746 was running out of time and space.

Altitude 15,000 feet. The air was heavier. It was now or never.

Duescher told Anderson to increase power slightly. The turbines howled above the noise of the Mach warning bell.

The nose came up, almost imperceptibly, but up.

More power, applied with the delicately careful skill of a surgeon's knife. The nose inched upward. Now both pilots gingerly hauled back on the control yoke and this time they felt response. Like a stilled heart massaged back to life, the elevators were reacting.

Altitude 14,000. Thirteen. Twelve.

The nose was level. Airspeed was normal. The lights of O'Neill winked placidly at the jet above, in innocent ignorance of what had almost happened.

Flight 746 crawled back to 15,000 feet and continued to Chicago after Duescher advised ATC that the emergency was over.

The 53 shaken passengers disembarked at O'Hare Airport. When Duescher left the plane, some of them booed him—unaware that his coolness and resistance to panic had saved them.

United, FAA, and CAB officials swarmed over the plane, looking for any sign of structural damage. Not a rivet had popped. The flight recorder was yanked and its tracings examined. *They were virtually identical to those of a Northwest Boeing 720 that had disintegrated in a Florida thunderstorm exactly five months before.*

The Northwest plane had slammed into the same combination of a violent updraft-downdraft vise over the

Everglades, shortly after takeoff from Miami. All aboard were killed and what actions the crew had taken will never be known for sure. But Boeing, in a special report on the NWA accident distributed to all 707-720 operators, said structural failure occurred after an apparent attempt to return the elevators to an up position while the jet was diving in an extreme nose-down attitude. The turbulence itself was insufficient to have caused structural failure, Boeing said.

Then-President W. A. Patterson of United wrote a personal letter to every passenger who had been on Flight 746. "I am sure the experience was frightening, to say the least," Patterson conceded. "If we are to be deserving of your confidence, we must be completely frank in providing you with the facts involved in such an incident. . . ."

Patterson then went on to relate the circumstances in detail. Speaking of Duescher in particular, and being well aware of the airport boos, the UAL chief added:

"I don't know of any experience where a flight officer kept his head and under such a severe experience had the knowledge of what not to do under such conditions. We can all be grateful to him for the deliberate and coolheaded manner in which he handled and solved such a critical emergency."

A few weeks later, Patterson invited Duescher and his crew to lunch. He handed each man a check amounting to five figures. But Duescher, who remembered those boos, was even more grateful for the letter.

The airline pilot offers the most incongruous contrast in aviation—he is the father image to many and an overpaid bus driver to others. He is variously portrayed as the stern-faced, tight-jawed God of the cockpit and a stewardess-chasing lecher with the morals of a tomcat. He is simultaneously regarded as a dedicated professional and a spoiled prima donna.

It is only too easy to generalize, but in truth the average airline pilot *does* have something of a dual personality. Even his union, the Air Line Pilots Association, wears two hats. It is a tough-talking labor union but it also is a dignified professional organization of considerable technical influence, one whose contributions to air safety have never been fully appreciated. And many, if not most, pilots seem to reflect ALPA's own double image.

The majority, for example, can be as belligerent and anti-management as a steelworker or truck driver during contract negotiations. Yet ALPA is the only union in the United States whose members are overwhelmingly Republican; one of the strongest and most vocal groups supporting Barry Goldwater in 1964 was a "Pilots for Goldwater" committee organized by a number of captains. The relative affluence of the airline pilot is largely responsible for his conservatism. It has been said that ALPA is the only union whose members ride to a picket line in Cadillacs.

Quite a few pilots (and I know some myself) suffer from acrophobia, or fear of height—when they are *not* flying, it should be added. This is not unusual, by the way; I love to fly, but I can't step out on a high-level balcony and look down without breaking into a cold sweat.

The many contradictions of an airline pilot's character make generalizations sometimes unfair. Among airline people themselves, pilots have acquired a reputation for stinginess that would make Jack Benny resemble the last of the big-time spenders. I know of one captain, with an annual salary of well over $20,000, who will walk through a restaurant picking up unclaimed tips from unoccupied tables. Yet the penurious pilot has a logical reason for seeming cheap; flight crews have a built-in sense of financial insecurity, and well they might have. An airline pilot lives under constant fear of having his well-heeled world collapse overnight. A captain gets a stiff check ride every six months, as well as complete proficiency retraining. He also is exposed to a searching medical examination twice a year, and what would be a gentle "take it easier" piece of advice for the average person could mean a career death sentence for a pilot. Any wage earner would lean toward tightfistedness under this kind of pressure.

Conversely, most airline pilots can be sentimental, spontaneously generous, and totally loyal. They also tend to possess delightful senses of humor, quick wit, and a gift of sharp repartee, which not even the disciplinary demands of the jet age have been able to douse. They love to play practical jokes on stewardesses and enjoy having tricks played on them. Under severe stress, they have been known to produce unexpected wisecracks that dissipated tension like a hot sun devouring morning fog.

A few years ago, an air traffic controller had his hands

full on a stormy night with visibility and ceiling nudging minimums. Flights were stacked up all the way to what would have been normal cruising altitudes, and the pilots were hounding ATC for descent clearances, approach clearances, and landing clearances.

One harassed controller finally growled into a radio frequency heard by the majority of the impatient crews:

"I'll get you guys down as soon as I can. We're doing the best we know how."

Back came the voice of an unidentified pilot.

"Bullshit!" he said loudly.

The controller was furious; such language is forbidden, and in this case was blackly resented.

"Attention all flights!" the controller barked. "Who said that?"

There was a dramatic pause while the pilots pondered the horrible crime. One by one, they offered their pious denials.

"United 542, negative on the bullshit."

"American 5, negative on the bullshit."

"TWA 22, negative on the bullshit."

"Northwest 301, negative on the bullshit."

"Continental 611, negative on the bullshit."

"Delta 419, negative on the bullshit."

"North Central 510, negative on the bullshit."

The roll call continued for a few more minutes and undoubtedly included a firm not-guilty from the offending flight. By the fourth or fifth response, the controller was laughing so hard he had to turn his mike over to a compatriot.

There was an equally tense situation involving one of the FAA's few female controllers. She was working flights in bad weather and experiencing communication difficulties. She finally asked one pilot, "Is my transmission fuzzy?"

Silence. Then a chuckle.

"I don't know, honey," the pilot replied. "How old are you?"

Airline pilots live by seniority, and their unofficial but time-honored slogan—"Seniority, Sex and Salary"—is more truth than fiction. A pilot's seniority number is vastly more important to him than his social security number, birthday, or even wedding anniversary. It governs the trips he flies, the type of equipment on which he works, the hours on which he is on duty, and the days off he gets. The average airline captain has a career span of about twenty-five years and the climb up the seniority ladder makes scaling Mount Everest a sprint race by comparison. Up until recently, it took most copilots eight years from date of hire before they achieved enough seniority to qualify for upgrading to the left seat. They don't have to wait as long these days, due to the rapid growth of air travel, the mandatory retirement-at-sixty rule imposed by the government, and the subsequent expansion of the pilot force.

In fact, some first officers are going over to the left seat in as short a period as three or four years. TWA has one young captain whose father also flies for the same airline. The youngster, an excellent pilot, actually qualified for captain in less than four years and at the tender age of twenty-three. His final checkride for upgrading to the fourth stripe resulted in a long list of commendations for his performance, with a minor exception—his cabin PA announcements. The check captain's comment on this phase read simply:

"His PA's will improve when his voice changes."

The public may well ask if faster promotion of young pilots constitutes a safety hazard. The answer is an unqualified negative. For one thing, rookie copilots hired by airlines are not exactly rookies. The minimum requirement for a new hiree is 500 hours of logged flight time, a commercial license, and an instrument rating—not to mention the toughest physical and mental tests known to industry. Most carriers go far beyond this minimum, accepting only applicants with at least 2,000 hours of multi-engine and/or jet experience—which means the majority of new airline pilots come from the military.

In doing research for a novel about the airlines recently, I was privileged to join a new pilots' class at Western Airlines. There were 18 men in the group, 10 from the Navy and 8 with Air Force backgrounds. Not a man in the group had less than 3,000 hours of flight time—yet Western's training was basic, the equivalent of putting an All-American football player through the fundamentals of blocking and tackling when he joins a professional team. And the class itself respected this tactic of "treat 'em like beginners."

"From the very first interview," one pilot remarked, "they got across the idea that airline flying is something special—with safety coming ahead of everything else. I thought I was pretty hot stuff until they began ramming a few facts down my throat."

Western also permitted me to observe the grueling checkride given to new first officers qualifying for the right seat on Boeing 737s—otherwise known as "Fat Albert" to carriers operating the stubby little jet. The experience was an eye-opener and gave me additional reason to feel reassured every time I fly commercially.

The two pilots whose airborne gauntlet I shared somewhat vicariously were 737 second officers, actually the third man in a cockpit designed to be operated by a captain and first officer. The presence of a third crew member was the result of a bitter controversy between ALPA and airlines flying 737s, the pilots' union insisting that the cockpit workload in the small Boeing necessitated a third crew member whose primary duty was to look out for other traffic. This pilot-airline battle will be discussed later; it is mentioned at this point to explain the 737 upgrading process of Western and other 737 operators. WAL's 737 hirees go through three weeks of ground school, and then fly as the third crew member until first officer seniority opens up. They then go back to additional ground school plus flight training that includes voluminous simulator and actual cockpit experience. The pilots I watched were "GIBS" (for Guys In Back, the sobriquet Western crews hung on the third man) who had completed the second phase of ground school and all flight training except for the final checkride.

(The term GIB is strictly unofficial and rather frowned on by Western officials. It seems somebody was browsing through a dictionary and discovered that a gib is a castrated tomcat.)

This particular duo reported for preflight briefing at 6 A.M. on a humid Saturday—the briefing consisting of Check Captain Smitty Dent's laconic instructions on what would be covered during the ride, plus some staccato questioning on certain emergency procedures that the checkride wouldn't cover because it was obviously impossible to have such real emergencies as an engine fire.

Samples of Dent's verbal interrogation:

"You've got an electrical fire. What are your procedures?"

"Tell me how to make a cross-bleed start."

"What can you do about a brake fire?"

"You got smoke in the cockpit—what's your first step?"

The answers have to be more than right; they must be fast. A mild frown, a gentle rebuke from Dent carries the same impact as an angry reaming.

The checkride was the same as Western gives first officers upgrading to captain.

"You gotta make 'em think like captains," Dent explained soberly. "If a guy figures he's being checked out just as a copilot, he'll do only what he has to. We want these kids to take the initiative, to get a feeling of command responsibility, even if it's years before they'll fly in that left seat."

Check captains like Dent must walk a very thin tightrope between toughness and patience—impressing a trainee with the seriousness of a checkride and yet humanly recognizing and tolerating natural nervousness.

"If you bust a maneuver," he warned these two youngsters, "don't panic. Very few training rides are perfect. Roll with the punches. I don't want to put undue pressure on you, but I still want you to bear in mind that I'm judging your ability to meet Western's standards for handling any kind of abnormal situation. If you fall short of any standard, it won't be the end of the world. I'll point out your mistakes, make sure you understand why you goofed, and we'll go through it again."

Gentle firmness describes Captain Dent. Even before takeoff, he scolded one pilot for an inadequate cockpit check that failed to catch an inoperative circuit breaker. But he accomplished this chastisement in a way that left the rookie mad at himself, not Dent.

The checkride started at 7 A.M. For the next five hours, with the trainees alternating at the controls, Dent threw the book at them.

Proper checklist and engine-start procedures. Correct takeoff clearances. Takeoffs. Engine-out procedures. Stall recovery. Emergency descents. High-rate descent and recovery. Steep turns. Slow flight. Engine fire shutdown and restart. Fire in the APU (Auxiliary Power Unit). Runaway stabilizer. Instrument Landing System (ILS) approach with an aborted landing. Single-engine ILS approach. Engine failure on takeoff prior to V_1. Engine failure on takeoff after V_1. Engine-out landing. Approach with no flaps. Approach with a jammed stabilizer. Approach with autopilot.

There were 38 items on the checkride grading sheet. Twenty-three of them were conducted in the air. The rest were fired at the pilots in a verbal examination.

Occasionally, the youngsters had to repeat a maneuver when Dent wasn't satisfied.

"Let's try it again," he told one who had fouled up a steep turn. "You didn't make sure you had a forty-five-degree bank on your indicator, and you waited until you were through thirty-degrees before you applied power."

The other pilot was sloppy on a landing approach.

"You asked for forty-degree flaps too soon," Dent chided quietly. "Try twenty-five on base, then thirty and go to forty on your turn into final."

The mistakes were noticeably more frequent toward the end of the five hours; fatigue and accumulated strain were taking their toll. Dent maintained both his pressure and his patience, deftly mixing praise with criticism.

"Come on a little smoother with that speed brake . . . that turn was within tolerance, but I'd like to see you try it again—you started out at forty-five degrees but you flattened out a bit . . . now, that was a touch of class when you got that mask on—fast and smooth."

Passengers who ignore oxygen mask demonstrations should have been along on this ride to see how hard Dent hammered home the importance of quick mask donning. One trainee was somewhat slow and hesitant during a maneuver involving emergency descent following loss of cabin pressure.

"Let's do it again," he ordered. "At thirty-five thousand feet if you lose pressure you've got fifteen seconds to save your life and the lives of one hundred seven passengers. That mask is the only thing between you and real trouble."

A debriefing followed the training ride. Dent went over their strong points and their weak points, this time shifting gears slightly. He emphasized the former without instilling in them any reason for cockiness or overconfidence.

"Now it's your turn," he smiled. "Any comments? Any questions?"

"I think there was room for improvement on my part," one pilot said. "Mainly on patterns."

"Your high work wasn't bad," Dent assured him. "Even FAA requires a passing grade of only seventy and I graded you about seventy-five on the first try. You got a ninety-five on the second which explains why I had you do it over."

"What you told us on the other training flights," the second pilot remarked. "Things sort of fell into place today. I wasn't behind the airplane. I felt good."

"And you should feel good now, after what I put you through," Dent said. "In all honesty, if you were being rated for your ATR [Air Transport Rating, required for all captains], I would have worked on you a little more. Like your circling approach, Tom. And Dick's patterns. But overall, you did a hell of a job. I liked Tom's decision to go around when he came in high that time. Touch of class. Real class. We're looking for guys who can act fast when things get hairy. Hell, anybody can screw up a maneuver. The important thing is that he recognizes that something's wrong and can do something about it in a hurry. Now, did anything happen today that you didn't like on my part? Did I confuse you at any time? Don't be bashful, dammit. Tell me."

"Well," one pilot said cautiously like a little boy about to correct his teacher, "on the flight before this one you jumped me for too tight a circling approach. Today you said I wasn't tight enough."

"You're allowed a one and a half mile margin," Dent said placidly. "I just wanted you to slow down a little. That's why today was so rough. Mostly critical maneuvers, when you gotta put it on the line. Like that one approach, Dick, with an engine out—if I hadn't called out airspeed, you would have sunk. I didn't bust you because you corrected. You got that nose up and you were fast to apply power. I hope you both learned one thing: to get an airplane to perform the way you want, fly her the way it was designed to fly. Any more questions? Observations? Okay, you both passed."

The two pilots rose, their young faces suddenly alive with relief—and pride. They were trying hard not to grin, but they weren't succeeding too well. As they left Dent's little office, their shoulders were straight and they somehow looked taller.

Dent sipped coffee and smiled slightly himself.

"I get a kick out of this job on days like this," he mused. "Rather be back flying the line but when you check out a couple of good kids like them and you know they'll make fine captains some day, you get a feeling of accomplish-

86

ment. This was only their fourth flight. Jesus, on the first one they didn't know their ass from third base. They were all thumbs. You notice them today? Sharp. Real sharp. Hell, I'd recommend 'em both for an ATR."

On their training record sheets, he filled in a section marked "Instructor Comments." His report was identical for both men.

"Good flight. Handles aircraft well. Knows procedures. Excellent attitude. See no problems. Recommend upgrading to F/O."

I put my notes in my pocket and walked with Dent to the Western parking lot. I heard the squeal of automobile brakes, followed by a loud thump and the crash of metal against metal. Dent and I watched the two drivers emerge from their cars, red-faced as they began to make angry inspections of damage.

I thought of the many times people who fear flying have said to me:

". . . but in an airplane, I gotta sit back in the cabin, helpless, depending on some other guy to do the right thing. Now in my own car, *I'm* in charge of the situation. . . ."

Professional airmen have a camaraderie, a spirit of comradeship, that transcends the rivalry among their hotly competitive airlines. One can see this at ALPA safety forums, where there is a solid closing of ranks on safety issues and where pilots seem to lose their individual airline identities in favor of a vague kind of fraternalism. Any emergency encountered by one pilot will invoke automatic and immediate cooperation from fellow airmen. Airline crews are often bitter toward private pilots, resenting the fact that a tiny Cessna or Piper on a nonessential, one-man pleasure flight can hold up a transport with a hundred passengers during peak traffic hours. Yet the FAA's files are full of incidents in which airline pilots have gone out of their way to guide lost, inexperienced, and panic-stricken private pilots to safety. Typical was this partial dialogue between a United captain and the pilot of a small plane who got into bad weather without instrument training and became not only disoriented but frightened to the point of total panic.

UAL: *"Do you read now?"*
Pilot: *"I read you but I don't know what I'm doing."*

UAL: *"Okay now, just relax. We all get in a spot once in a while. If you'll just relax your hands on the wheel, just for a second, I think we'll calm down. Take your feet off the rudders for a second and then just shake your hands a bit and relax and go back to it and just head east, which is 'E' on the indicator. East heading and hold that for a minute or so. Just nice and straight and I think we can calm down quite a bit and accomplish quite a bit. Okay?"*

Pilot: *"Okay, I got you."*

UAL: *"You have a good airplane under you. It's a real good machine and with just a little help, it will do a real good job for you."*

Pilot: *"We are going due east now at nine thousand feet."*

Pilot: *"Very good, very good. Just hold that now and you'll be doing real good."*

Pilot: *"My gas is getting down below a quarter of a tank."*

UAL: *"We all make mistakes. Relax now, and we'll get you out of this . . ."*

Thanks to the United crew, the Traffic Control Center in the area, and a more experienced private pilot who took over a little later from United, the lost airman landed safely.

There has been an admirable improvement in relations between pilots and controllers, a steadily growing mutual appreciation of each other's problems and needs. Tempers occasionally get short, nerves become frayed, and there can be angry exchanges—usually when airports and airways get clogged. But airmen have mounting respect for the men who work in those antiseptic pressure cookers that are the towers and control centers. Many pilots visit ATC facilities in an FAA-ALPA-airline program aimed at acquainting pilots with the work of controllers. In turn, more and more controllers are taking advantage of "FAM" (familiarization) flights—the privilege of riding in airliner cockpits to obtain firsthand knowledge of pilot procedures. (7)

It is impossible to cast the airline pilot in a single mold. If anything, the membership of ALPA and the Allied Pilots Association (APA is a pilots' union that represents American Airlines flight crews exclusively) is in essence a collection of rugged individualists. Pilots simply refuse to be typecast and they vary in personalities probably as widely as any other professional cross section in America. Some are inveterate clowns and some are deadly serious, occasionally on the dour side. Some are deeply religious, community-minded, and devoted family men. Others are admitted playboys. Many try to forget aviation between trips. But a sizable minority are hard workers in the field of safety—the contributions of the pilot group toward greater air safety are sadly underrated. Many aviation reforms have stemmed directly from pilots' demands, suggestions, and even experiment and research conducted on their own time. And in many cases, flight crew thinking on safety has been years ahead of government and industry, particularly in the pre-jet era. Airborne radar, the need for modernized air traffic control, better runway lighting, and improved navigation aids are just a few examples.

ALPA has been criticized, with some justification, for its rather one-sided, almost totally subjective approach to crash investigations; its representatives on accident-probing teams seem to be concerned solely with efforts to defend crews from charges of pilot error. But there also is some justification for this provincialism. An erring pilot too frequently is the victim of sins of omission and/or commission perpetrated by somebody outside the cockpit, in the form of inadequate tools. It cannot be said too often that very few crashes have a single cause. Most are the culmination of circumstances and mistakes that cannot always be laid in the lap of the airman who makes the final error resulting in an accident. If ALPA invariably tries to defend pilots, in effect it also is asking *why* a crash occurred, not merely *how*. Until recent years, the history of crash investigation was replete with cases of pilots blamed for accidents while no effort was made to look for the reasons they goofed.

A couple of years ago, a Delta Air Lines plane undershot a runway at a small southern airport. Fortunately there were no fatalities but the captain, Keith D. Heefner, was threatened with loss of his ATR for allowing his first officer to make a poorly executed approach. It was, as the FAA hearing officer phrased it, a classic example of an accident "occurring in circumstances which apparently indicate no malfunctioning of the aircraft, and no unusual weather phenomenon, or any act of God or other circumstances beyond the control of the pilot-in-command, that might reasonably account for the accident."

Heefner himself, in fact, readily admitted the approach was bad—an inevitable confession inasmuch as the plane did crash. But he insisted it *seemed* to be a normal approach and that his copilot, who was flying the aircraft, also was unaware they were too low until they touched down about 120 feet short of the runway. Heefner's fellow Delta pilots, led by safety representative Vic Hewes, did some investigating of their own.

Captain Hewes is an ex-RAF pilot whose British accent is about as incongruous among Delta's Atlanta-based crews as a southern drawl would sound in London. He served as ALPA's representative during the National Transportation Safety Board's investigation of the Heefner accident, but he did some hard probing of his own— enough to challenge the official charges of pilot error.

Hewes, a big, friendly, extrovertish type of man who has worked on more crashes and safety problems than he likes to admit, argued that if both pilots *thought* they were making a normal approach while actually making a poor one, there had to be a reason. He found it—an optical illusion applicable to this particular airport under certain conditions and circumstances.

He showed that the airport was constructed in such a way that a pilot approaching from the west, using the runway on which Heefner was landing, could easily feel that the runway slopes away from him when it actually rises. Using photographs, diagrams, and maps, Hewes demonstrated how the illusion could occur. The runway, he explained, rises from the west for a distance of about 1,200 feet; then dips slightly to a point some 2,200 feet from the west end; and finally rises again the remainder of its 4,500 feet.

"The effect created by this and attendant conditions, particularly the terrain at the two ends of the runway," Hewes went on, "is that in making a normal three-degree approach from the west, the angle to the overall inclined runway is approximately four and a half degrees. As a result, a pilot making an approach in that direction would naturally think he was higher than he actually was."

(Coming from the opposite direction, the same terrain could trick a pilot into believing he was too low.)

Hewes testified that this illusion is heightened considerably at night (Heefner was making a night approach) because the terrain to the west falls off rapidly, from a point only 100 feet from the end of the runway and into a depression that is 100 feet lower than the runway. This depression is covered by trees and has no lights which might give a pilot some terrain reference. The terrain at the east end rises rather abruptly, another factor in heightening the illusion.

The culminating factor in creating the dangerous illusion, Hewes pointed out, was the low overcast present on the night Heefner's landing went wrong.

The FAA suggested that Heefner didn't pay proper attention to his instruments and that he was tardy in lowering the flaps. But the FAA's hearing officer, in a decision that cleared the crew of pilot error charges, pointed out that in a visual approach it is entirely proper for a pilot to use instruments only as a cross-check—once he has the runway in sight. Heefner's main means of monitoring his copilot's glide path was the visual reference of the runway lights—an erroneous reference, the hearing officer agreed, which was due to the illusion Hewes proved could have existed.

As for the flaps, the hearing officer reminded the FAA that delayed flaps would have led to an overshoot, not an undershoot. He conceded that Captain Hewes did not prove Heefner was the victim of an illusion, but he ruled that Hewes did prove its possibility—thus negating pilot error and charges of careless airmanship. And the officer added this comment:

". . . the Air Line Pilots Association is to be commended and congratulated for its efforts to find what may prove to be the answer to otherwise unexplained aviation accidents involving short landings. While I am sure the Association is reluctant to find pilot error and is always interested in establishing some other explanation, this, of course, is entirely natural and proper and I feel may very well serve an excellent purpose. Perhaps, as indicated in this case, the studies being made will reveal that optical illusion is a very real danger and possibility and will lead to corrective measures, increasing the safety of aviation."

The Heefner incident was, in truth, relatively minor and hardly known outside of air safety circles. But both as an example and a precedent, its significance is major. Here we had the FAA itself, through its own hearing examiner, reverse a pilot error finding because somebody went beyond the error and found out why it was committed. Here was a situation in which the airport was found guilty instead of the pilot and, as the hearing officer suggested, it is only fair to ask how many previous cases of alleged pilot error could have resulted in crash prevention if the investigators had not been satisfied merely with attaching a stigma to an airman's name. It is an aviation axiom that most crashes occur on landing and another axiom that most landing accidents are blamed on the crews. Now, at last, safety experts are starting to read between the lines of those two axioms—for the latter is more of an assumption than an axiom.

Heefner and Hewes alike were lucky that the crew walked away from this one. A prime reason for inadequate, incomplete pilot error decisions has been the obvious inability of investigators to question dead airmen. In such cases, they often are convicted by circumstantial evidence.

Pilots *do* make mistakes, some of them inexcusable, careless, and occasionally fatal. But they do *not* make deliberate mistakes and frequently their "sins" are wrong decisions, forged under the heat of split-second judgments and sudden emergency. This is why they so deeply resent pilot error verdicts that blame without further probing. The evidence keeps mounting that research into the causes of pilot error will pay off huge safety dividends, and in the next chapter we will examine one such area of research conducted by Boeing.

One thing pilots dread as well as resent is the layman's occasional judgment of flying technique. Most passengers tend to rate an airman by the landing he makes, which is grossly unfair inasmuch as very few pilots can "paint a plane" on a runway everytime; there are too many variables involved in the landing phase, and those who murmur "lousy landing" when an airliner comes in hard or bouncy should realize the difficulties of putting a 120-ton monster down gently and smoothly in the middle of a stiff crosswind, on a runway that is too short and greased with rain, snow, or ice.

Too often, however, uninformed criticism of pilots by passengers has crept into accident hearings. A few years ago, a DC-7 crashed while trying to land in a heavy fog so thick that the fire engines couldn't find the burning wreckage for thirty minutes. One of the surviving passengers testified that the pilot had announced over the PA system, before landing, that "I'll get you down on the ground—or in it." He was the only survivor to produce this damaging quote and not a few of the dead captain's colleagues would have thoroughly enjoyed meeting this example of self-importance in a locked room.

In hearings on another crash, a surviving witness claimed that the pilot had flown right over the airport before the crash, which occurred on letdown prior to final approach.

"He obviously was lost," the witness proclaimed, adding that he himself could see the lights of the airport directly below the plane. If this passenger saw any lights, he was the only one and it wasn't the airport because investigators proved the plane never got close to the field before the accident took place.

Some passengers actually write letters to the CAB and FAA complaining about poor flying, although the majority of them apparently derived their aeronautical knowledge from watching John Wayne movies. Pilots accept these as an occupational hazard, but rightfully burn up when such letters wind up in a semiofficial investigation and even a carpet session. One example will suffice: I know a captain who made a normal close-in approach, involving a fairly steep turn to line up with the runway. It was about as dangerous as turning a corner in an automobile at 10 miles an hour, and completely routine.

A passenger wrote the FAA that the pilot had endangered lives with "a turn that practically threw us out of our seats." The unsigned letter was turned over to the chief pilot who asked the captain for an explanation. The captain offered two observations, one of which questioned the decency of investigating an incident on the basis of an unsigned complaint, and the other which suggested where the FAA and the chief pilot could stick the letter.

Pride in their profession and the skills required is one more item pilots have in common. Another is real profession, an almost mystical appreciation of flight that can be grasped only by those fortunate enough to share that love. (Many stewardesses do, which is why pilot-stewardess marriages usually are successful.)

Their infatuation with flight is a common bond, an emotional explanation for the unanimous bitterness veteran pilots feel toward the controversial "retire at sixty" rule imposed by the FAA in 1959. A layman would find it a fascinating experience to attend the conventions of retired-pilot organizations—several airlines have such groups.

American's "Grey Eagles" was the first and is one of the biggest and most active. If you could be present at one of the annual gatherings of the Eagles, you would notice first of all the above-average physical condition of the recently retired members—those the FAA forced to quit, even though they were (and many still are) capable of passing any flight or medical test.

A few have potbellies, while some look like men only a couple of years beyond a professional football career. All have the telltale crow's-feet around their eyes, that hallmark of men who fly. Typically, the three-day convention agenda schedules only one business meeting, with the rest of the time set aside for fun.

Wander around them and you pick up such snatches of conversation as:

"Yeh, I remember my first flight. We had three passengers and all of 'em got airsick. . . ."

". . . Remember old Captain So-and-so? I flew with him six months before the creep let me make a landing. . . ."

". . . You had troubles your first trip? Hell, mine was back in '30—between New York and Hartford. Thunder and lightning all the way in weather I wouldn't have driven a car in . . . I couldn't find Hartford 'til we were on the ground. . . ."

". . . You're damned right I remember my first engine failure—I couldn't forget it because it didn't happen until I had twenty-six thousand hours logged. . . ."

They reminisce and swap tales and they can be forgiven if the years have colored a few yarns brighter than the real event. Their nostalgia runs a curious pattern. Most remember their first airline flight with amazingly vivid clarity —some can even give you the name of the stewardess—yet memories are hazy about more recent years.

Almost to a man, they talk warmly—and occasionally with a kind of wry awe—about the various captains they flew with when they were young pilots. The martinets, the practical jokers, the ones who imparted wisdom. Seldom do they mention the present—only the past, because the past was flying and the present is usually nothing but a memory of happier years. It is not that they are inactive.

94

The majority of the Eagles' 400 members are in occupations ranging from real estate to operating golf courses. Many have turned their avocations of airline days into vocations in their new lives; again, the propensity of pilots to have a kind of "reserve" business is a manifestation of their financial insecurity, their constant dread of the day when they will be unable to fly.

No pilot has really resented being grounded because of health—usually eyesight, reaction time, or heart. But he does get indignant at the prospect of retiring before he wants to—under what he regards as an arbitrary age limit established on a questionable correlation between chronological and physiological age. While it is true that a man in his sixties is theoretically more vulnerable to a heart attack than one much younger, actual experience under the FAA's retirement rule offers absolutely no valid support. Between 1952 and 1967 16 U.S. airline pilots died while on duty. The average age was only 43.5, and the chronological breakdown is interesting:

Age bracket	Number of deaths
under 30	1
30–39	4
40–49	7
50–59	4

Talk to a recently retired Grey Eagle or any other physically fit airline pilot hit by mandatory retirement and you can understand their bitterness; you'll probably begin to share it, because these grizzled veterans can be intensely persuasive.

"Look around this room," one says to you. "You can find men over sixty who can pass any physical examination and any proficiency flight check better than half the men flying today. The airlines are short of pilots, the supply is going to get tighter, and the government still won't let them tap all this experience. It's the most criminal, inexcusable, inefficient waste of manpower in American industry."

"It's a bunch of malarkey that a pilot over sixty is more likely to have a heart attack," adds another retiree, who looks capable of wrestling a bear. "Any doctor will tell you the most dangerous years for a sudden, unexpected major coronary are between forty and fifty, not past sixty. It would have been fairer if FAA had just tightened medical and proficiency tests for older captains and then let the airlines themselves set a retirement age based on individual pension plans."(8)

When FAA put the retirement rule into effect in 1959, only 40 captains were affected immediately. But now, each year finds a soaring number of pilots reaching sixty.

ALPA early in 1968 in vain petitioned the FAA to drop the mandatory retirement rule and allow pilots who are sixty or over to keep flying so long as they can pass medical and proficiency tests. The union argued with commendable logic that many of the reasons for forced retirement cited in 1959 no longer are valid. There is no large group of older pilots facing difficult transition from pistons to jets. Many jetliners have three qualified pilots in the cockpit, reducing the hazards of incapacitation. And finally, premature retirement may work against safety. The pilot group is getting older. Nearly 75 percent of ALPA's 1967 membership roster was in the forty-to-fifty-nine age bracket. By 1972, nearly 6,000 airline pilots will be in the fifty-to-fifty-nine age group, compared with 2,200 in 1967 and only 315 in 1959.

This means that if mandatory retirement at sixty stays on the books, the airlines in another five years will be losing a huge pool of their most experienced and skilled cockpit personnel—and this with the critical years of jumbos coming up by 1970. President Floyd Hall of Eastern estimates that it costs an airline $200,000 to qualify a three-man crew for the Boeing 747, thus raising the unpleasant prospect of spending millions on training pilots who start flying the 747 shortly before they have to retire. And it will be the veterans, not the younger pilots, who will be operating 747 trips. This is one issue in which ALPA has drawn general airline support.

One intriguing proposal is to give pilots sixty and over limited supervisory service on the jumbo jets and supersonic airliners. Under this plan, older captains would oversee flight operations in the cockpits of the giant jets but would not fly the plane except in occasional relief or in the event of the regular captain's incapacitation. Literally, he would be in the same role as a ship's captain who walks the bridge and monitors crew performances, without ever performing manual duties himself.

The plan seems to have much merit, although it carries

the initial drawback of adding a large sum to operating costs of the jumbos and supersonics. A senior captain qualified on the Boeing 747 will be making nearly $60,000 a year. One flight a week for our hypothetical "supervisory captain" would cost an airline about $5,000 beyond normal crew salaries. The question to be settled is whether this expense would be justified in terms of added safety.

It may be that the older pilots would accept reduced pay for admittedly lesser duties—just as they accept salary reductions when they take ground jobs with airlines. Also to be decided is whether this "flight foreman" would be in actual command of the aircraft, or whether he would be acting in purely an advisory role with the regular left-seater retaining command authority. The relationship between captains and these older men could be touchy, even if the authority of each was spelled out contractually.

An increasingly older pilot population must be considered a part of what has yet to be but might become a major safety problem—fatigue.

The average layman is likely to have a somewhat jaundiced view of any man who gets paid up to $59,000 a year for working about seventy hours a month. There is little doubt, however, that 70 hours of duty in the cockpit of a jetliner are more than the equivalent of the usual 40-hours-a-week job in terms of fatigue as well as responsibility. It was thirty years ago that the airlines agreed to limit monthly flight time to 85 hours. That maximum stayed in effect up to the sixth year of the jet age, when the airlines conceded that the jets had created new fatigue problems not anticipated six years before.

One obvious difference is the speed of the jetliner. A pilot flying a piston schedule used to make 5 round-trip transcontinental flights per month to get in his 85 hours. On the faster jets, 85 hours would add up to 10 flights a month.

Another fatigue factor is purely medical. Jet crews literally live in an atmosphere where cold outside air is pumped into the aircraft, warmed, and then expelled rapidly. Such air is almost totally lacking in moisture. This results in a dehydration process which causes loss of potassium from the blood stream and body tissue over a long period. Such a loss can lead to abnormal fatigue.

Fatigue also is involved in what doctors term "diurnal variation"—man's habit of dividing his daily life into roughly three eight-hour periods, eight hours for sleep, eight for work, and eight for relaxation. International and transcontinental flight crews, exposed to frequent time zone changes, have this natural, habitual cycle disrupted almost continually. It usually takes three days to get back into the normal cycle, and there will be even more difficult readjustment when the supersonic age dawns.(9)

Finally, there is a certain amount of tension stemming from the jets themselves. They are marvelously efficient, strong, and dependable. But they demand more pilot attention and faster decisions—both fatigue-causing factors. I recently asked a captain who has been flying for three decades, including ten years of jets, if fatigue was a problem as far as he was concerned. He wrote me:

"Yes, flying jets takes a lot out of me. I haven't really been able to pin down all the reasons even in my own mind, but I'm bushed mentally and physically even after a relatively short flight. I guess the main reason for jet fatigue is that everything moves at such a fast pace. When a problem comes up and there's need for decision and action, you can't park and think it over. The manager of a multi-million-dollar factory must make important decisions, but he has time to consider them. Just move his multi-million-dollar factory through the air at high speed and the pressure is increased many times over."

The letter continued: "You fly the jet by the book and it's a damned thick book. To stay ahead of any jet, a pilot must stay mentally on the edge of his seat every minute. Take the landing approach, for example. In a typical jetliner, a pilot has only about 110 seconds from the outer marker to the runway. He's flying a machine that weighs about 100 tons and he's moving some 250 feet per second. Even on a normal, routine ILS approach, the pace and workload are high.

"Because of all this, many of the decisions and actions involved in control of the aircraft are irrevocable. Again, the pilot can't stop in mid-air and think them over."

In conclusion, the captain wrote: "I don't know of a single pilot who isn't tired when he gets off a trip, including the routine ones. You can't help being conscious of the fact that you've been operating five or six or seven million dollars' worth of airplane that's absolutely unforgiving of carelessness, bad judgment or poor flying technique. You carry that sense of responsibility around in your guts every second you're on the plane, and when the flight's over it's still sitting inside you like an undigested meal.

"Sure, we fly as few as seventy hours a month. Sounds easy, doesn't it? But three or four hours in a jet is the equivalent of eight or nine hours of hard work, and when I say work I mean mental strain as well as physical exertion. You ask if I get tired? Hell, yes!"

Buttressing the view of this pilot was a survey made a couple of years ago among wives of jet captains flying for two major airlines. The wives were selected instead of their husbands to avoid any reluctance of the men to admit weaknesses, symptoms, and physical difficulties. The returned questionnaires disclosed a significant percentage of increasing nervous tension, as portrayed by the wives' complaints. They reported their husbands showing less interest in their children, in recreation, and in sex since they began flying jets. Some of this may have been due to the normal aging process, but the responses indicated that fatigue and stress were going beyond the expectable.

"His fatigue, both physical and emotional, seems to be what would be expected over a 10–15 year period, not three years," one wife wrote.

"He's on a treadmill of flying and sleeping, never quite catching up," said another.

"It takes all of his three days off to get rested up for the next trip," a spouse complained.

No comment is necessary on the following observation:

"There is an anti-social, irritable stranger living in this house and you can have him. I want laughing boy back."

Fatigue probably played a contributing role in an accident involving a Japan Air Lines DC-8 at San Francisco, a night approach in poor weather, and the pilots literally flying their aircraft into the water. They had been on duty for about ten hours. (The captain of the JAL plane later shouldered the entire blame, admitted to an improperly executed instrument approach, and went on Japanese television where he apologized to JAL and the Japanese people for his mistake. He then tore up his ATR and voluntarily took a demotion to flight engineer with the announced intention of working his way back up the ladder to the left seat! One finds it hard to imagine a U.S. captain, or any pilot other than a Japanese, displaying the same humility.)

It is somewhat difficult for pilots to "sell" the public on

99

such problems as fatigue, partially because of an old suspicion that economics is the ulterior motive behind many pilot safety proposals. Here again is that contradictory double image of ALPA—when airmen fight for some safety measure, are they speaking as skilled, objective technicians, or as union members masquerading a labor demand under the guise of a safety problem?

Typical was ALPA's fight to put a third man in the cockpit of the twin-engine Boeing 737, on the contention that he was needed for collision protection and to handle any unusual emergency arising in the cabin. United pilots were the first to propose what the airlines promptly labeled featherbedding, which in a sense it is. The 737 is the most automated jet flying today, specifically designed for a two-man crew. The addition of a third man, who literally is nothing more than a lookout and an extra cabin attendant should the need for the latter arise, meant an unwelcome jump in operating costs for airlines which ordered the 737 on the premise it was an efficient two-man airplane. (Western alone is shelling out $1 million annually for the third man.)

United set the pattern for the rest of the industry when it agreed to operate some of its new 737s with three men, while other 737 flights were flown with the normal two-man complement. At the end of a year, an impartial board would rule on the need for the third man based on studies of comparative workload, the efficiency of the additional pilot in preventing near-misses and collisions, and other safety factors. Other carriers said they would abide by United's findings.

The special board, early in March of 1969, issued a report which settled the issue only partially and temporarily. It said the three-man crew on the 737 should be continued on all UAL flights "for the life of the current basic agreement between the parties, which has another year to run." In effect, the board agreed with the airlines that a third man wasn't needed very often but also agreed with ALPA that on some occasions, he could "make a significant contribution to the safety of the flight." It suggested that further research was needed for a final determination.

The board can be excused for not taking a definite stand, for the third-man issue is about as clear-cut as fog. There is not the slightest doubt in the world that a third crew member is an added safety measure. But in fighting for his adoption on all 737 flights, why didn't ALPA also insist on his presence in other two-man jets—the DC-9 and BAC-111? The cockpit workload on these aircraft is just as heavy as in the 737 and possibly even greater. Some ALPA officials admit privately that this inconsistency is the weakest link in their case and they bemoan the union's approval of DC-9 and BAC-111 two-man contracts before United's crews raised the third-man question.

In fairness to all concerned, ALPA's fight for the third man on the 737 was based on experience with the earlier two-man jets—including one midair collision between a TWA DC-9 and a private plane, in which cockpit workload during the jet's final approach definitely contributed to the tragedy. But having brought up the whole issue, ALPA might reasonably be expected to question the advisability of operating *any* jetliner with less than two men. Certainly the whole affair is somewhat unfair to Boeing, which in good faith designed, built, and had certificated a two-man jet that is now tougher to sell for purely economic reasons. Even an airline which considered the 737 a superior aircraft might choose a DC-9 instead because of the extra expense of the third crew member on the former.

The third-man issue could be debated for another five hundred pages. But to this observer, it all adds up to a perfect example of ALPA's double image. Some DC-9 and BAC-111 contracts were negotiated for economic benefits, whereas 737 contracts had safety as the prime matter at stake. This is nothing but a double standard as far as ALPA is concerned; one can't blame UAL's pilots for the stand they took, but there is considerable temptation to criticize ALPA for literally taking two stands.

The union also is prone to be a little too thin-skinned and oversolicitous of its members. After a rash of landing and approach accidents in 1968 and 1969, Chairman Joseph J. O'Connell of the National Transportation Board saw fit to issue a warning to *all* aviation. He said the crashes would not have occurred if "all ground and airborne navigational systems (had) been operating accurately and had the flight crews been piloting with meticulous reference to properly indicating flight instruments."

O'Connell was understandably angered when ALPA promptly issued a statement complaining that he had inferred negligence on the part of crews. The ALPA release quoted only O'Connell's remark about "piloting with meticulous reference to properly indicating flight instruments" and failed to mention the chairman's equally strong finger of blame at faulty ground and air navigational systems.

"We are inferring nothing," O'Connell snapped. "There is a problem and we simply ask that all the possibilities, the man, the machine, and the environment be looked at again."

Which no pilot should have criticized, inasmuch as O'Connell in so many words was merely pleading for what pilots themselves have always requested: namely, an examination of *all* aspects of accidents, outside as well as inside the cockpit.

The same ALPA tendency to bristle at justified criticism was apparent after the breakup of a Braniff Electra in a thunderstorm May 3, 1968. The crew had been warned of severe turbulence ahead and also were advised that other flights were being vectored around the storm. The NTSB urged FAA to prohibit penetration of predicted thunderstorm activity and to require avoidance of severe storms by at least 20 nautical miles.

This brought from ALPA's 1968 safety forum the following resolution:

". . . that the Air Line Pilots Association hereby goes on record as opposing any official regulation, advisory or report which implies that operation by any airline pilot in such areas is in any way an exercise of poor judgment. Be it further resolved that any incidents involving flight through thunderstorm areas which result in other than smooth flight are deemed to be caused by the state of the art and not the result of poor judgment on the part of the pilot."

This was tantamount to ALPA's demanding "not-guilty" verdicts in advance of mishaps which *may* have involved bad judgment. Certainly there was nothing sacred about the NTSB recommendations; the Board is honest, dedicated, and efficient, but it is neither omnipotent nor always right. The FAA rejected the recommendations as impractical and they very well might have been. A mandatory 20-mile detour around all thunderstorms would disrupt schedules without adding much of a safety guarantee. Yet ALPA's forum resolution seemed to be a blank check drawn on the name of whatever pilot violated common sense and command judgment.

This is not to pass judgment on the Braniff captain,

who may have been the victim of mental fatigue rather than bad judgment. It is merely to suggest that if pilots want fair, totally objective crash investigations, they should be willing to concede that a pilot error verdict may be the right decision on some occasions.

Yet contrary to some critics, ALPA's conditioned reflex action to any suggestion of pilot error is not necessarily a union reflex; it is more often generated by the professional in a pilot, not the union member. ALPA recently spent $50,000 to clear a captain of charges that he endangered lives by losing control of a jet in unexpected turbulence. The captain was not even an ALPA member, although it could be argued that ALPA took his case because it didn't want any precedent set that might someday cost a member his job.

I have been defending ALPA and pilots for years because I believe and still believe that airline crews *do* deserve a large and loud voice in safety decisions. I believed and still believe that pilots are often ahead of everyone else in recognizing the existence of safety problems and in proposing reforms and solutions. Occasionally ALPA as a group and some pilots individually bother me with what I can best describe as a mild persecution complex—a kind of self-pity, a form of petulant resentment of authority (which is somewhat incongruous in itself because once an airman puts on that fourth stripe, he *is* Authority in the same sense a ship captain is a minor dictator in his own small world).

It is regulatory and management authority, of course, which the pilot resents and even fears and with a certain amount of logic. An FAA inspector can cut an airman's career prematurely short, and there undoubtedly are some inspectors who are unfair, arbitrary, and occasionally far less qualified and skillful than the man on whose flying ability they are passing judgment. But too many pilots are prone to overgeneralize in their resentment. I have known, for example, several hard-working ALPA members who were promoted to check captains. I cringed when I kept hearing their former colleagues refer to them as "just another management fink now."

This could be classed as another form of double standard. Pilots preach wisely that safety should never be compromised. They will not tolerate unsafe airports, inefficient air traffic control, petty government arrogance, airlines which try to cut corners, and overzealous check captains. Yet too many will tolerate colleagues who literally are accidents waiting to happen—who are known to drink too much, who are known to be marginal in ability, who are known to be careless and irresponsible, and who are known to be emotionally unstable. To blindly defend any pilot guilty of blatant carelessness or bad judgment is just as wrong as hanging an undeserved rap on an airman.

Several airlines are planning to install recording devices on jets that would depict exactly how a captain flies each trip. From the data collected over six months' operations, an airline could determine whether a pilot was consistently maintaining assigned altitudes, handling fuel flow efficiently, flying smooth and proper ILS approaches, etc. There would be 47 parameters of performance, each preset to an established margin of tolerance, giving chief pilots an exceptionally clear picture of whether crews were exceeding those margins.

Admittedly, this smacks of a "Big Daddy Is Watching You" gimmick. It has obvious advantages for an airline and it has some for pilots; six-month proficiency checks would be eliminated for captains whose computerized data showed a consistent level of good performance. But airmen are mapping a strong fight against any such device which might cost a pilot his job. Pilots feel that no "black box" can tell the entire story of a flight, because it cannot provide the reasons why a pilot may have exceeded established margins of operating techniques. They do not object to the proposed system, provided it is used solely to pinpoint weaknesses in training and proficiency test procedures and not as a means of spying on pilots for the purpose of punishment, harassment, or outright dismissal.

There are legitimate and logical pros and cons on the merits of what may become a pilot-airline donneybrook. Certainly, the system might catch a few pilots who aren't paragons of perfection when they are not under the watchful eyes of a check captain or an FAA inspector. On the other hand, many pilots—particularly the veterans with twenty-five and thirty years experience—are seriously concerned over too much "fly 'em by the book" training, of which the monitoring device is merely an extension. They fear that overregulation, overreliance on specific procedures and rules, are literally taking too much command judgment away from airmen.

"Fly 'em by the book is fine ninety-nine percent of the time," one 34,000-hour veteran told me. "But what happens on that rare occasion when the book doesn't cover the situation exactly? Or maybe the book's not quite right. Or what happens if you save lives by breaking a rule— as some pilots have done? Too many of the younger pilots simply won't use their own good sense, or they won't challenge any set procedure, because they've been brainwashed not to deviate in the slightest. Sure it works most of the time, but by God they'd better be able to break out of that mold if they have to."

Is this view the last-ditch cry of the older airmen who instinctively yearn for the days when seat-of-the-pants superseded any book? Or is it a plea from men who sincerely believe no rule is a substitute for common sense? There is no ready answer; only the personal observation that it is the rare pilot-sinner who keeps airline management and the FAA in the harassment business. There are some 25,000 airline pilots in the United States, but if only a tiny fraction of them stray from the reservation of duty, responsibility, and maturity, this handful muddies the image of all 25,000.

ALPA for some time has been concerned over its reputation in the nation's press. A few years ago, it asked a public relations consulting firm to conduct an extensive survey among leading aviation and labor writers. The union wanted to know what these newspapermen thought of airline pilots in general and ALPA in particular. The results were not cause for smugness. Less than 30 percent credited the organization with being a real force in promoting safety, while nearly all the respondents regarded ALPA primarily as a labor union. A disturbing 47 percent rated ALPA's image as fair, poor, or bad.

The survey obviously reflected some lack of knowledge about the nation's air crews and their contributions to safety. For one thing, a crash gets more publicity than a technical achievement—and most accidents eventually are blamed on the men up front.

Inasmuch as pilot error statistically is the leading cause of crashes, it is too bad there are no statistics on the number of times pilot skill has kept a disaster from occurring. Three particularly dramatic incidents have been described earlier. Others, just from the U.S. airlines, would fill a book. Men like Captain R. E. McKenna of United, who landed a DC-6 safely after a freak structural failure knocked off virtually his entire rudder. Or Captain David Rall of Northwest, who ditched a flaming DC-7 off the Philippines and lost only one passenger—an elderly woman with a heart condition.

Some comprehension of what it means not to have an accident happen—because a pilot has demonstrated courage, technical ability, and calmness under stress—can be gleaned from this Air Force data on average human reaction times in the air:

Time from eye image to brain	0.1 seconds
Recognition time of brain	1.0 seconds
Decision time	5.0 seconds
Decision time to muscle	0.4 seconds
Muscle reaction time	0.4 seconds
Air reaction time	5.0 seconds

This adds up to 11.9 seconds elapsing between the time the human eye spots an emergency situation and when the airplane itself responds to whatever decision the pilot has made. Remember that a jet in landing configuration—the slowest phase of flight—still is moving 250 feet per second. There have been too many accidents blamed on pilot error in which crews simply ran out of time in which to conquer an unexpected emergency—or "running out of information and altitude simultaneously," as pilots like to phrase it. Given a reasonable breathing space, the airline pilot can perform miracles.

One of the most unusual "saves" in aviation history occurred May 29, 1965, and it involved unprecedented pilot teamwork, ingenuity, and coordination—the safe landing of a crippled jet by using procedures developed in an emergency test flight a thousand miles away while the jet circled and awaited the results!

A Northwest Boeing 727, Flight 227 from Newark to Chicago, took off routinely but quickly ran into trouble. The crew had retracted the landing gear but the nose gear red warning light remained on. Captain Harry Muldoon ordered the gear dropped again to see if repeating the extension-retraction cycle would produce the green lights of normal operation. But with the gear supposedly down, the red warning light for an unlocked nosewheel kept glaring ominously at the pilots.

At this stage, Muldoon didn't know if the nosewheel was up *or* down. He flew over the Newark tower for a visual inspection and got the bad news immediately—the nose gear was fully retracted despite the extension cycle. Muldoon and his crew could not know the reason, of course, but they did know that some failure in the nose gear lock system had made extension impossible. They tried every conceivable normal and emergency extension system in the book; the nose gear stayed up, which meant that sooner or later Muldoon was going to have to land the 727 with its snout pushing up pieces of runway pavement.

Northwest requires its crews to notify headquarters in Minneapolis-St. Paul of any abnormal situation. The NWA Planning Office received Muldoon's message and alerted Captain Paul Soderlind, Superintendent of Flying. Soderlind, in turn, asked an engineering official named John Reiman to meet him at the Minneapolis Airport on the double. Reiman's title: Weight and Balance Engineer. Soderlind wanted his advice on what would be the key factor in saving Flight 227 from a potentially bad accident—reducing weight forward so the nose could be held off the ground as long as possible when the plane finally landed.

Both Soderlind and Reiman were uncomfortably aware that all concerned, including the airplane, were breaking new ground. No 727 had even suffered a stuck nose gear before. Boeing had furnished all 727 operators with a nose-up landing procedure, but Soderlind wasn't satisfied that it could provide minimum landing damage. He asked the Planning Office for a 727 to be used in an emergency test flight, and he began conferring with Reiman on what advice to give Muldoon.

"For one thing," the balance specialist suggested, "tell him to start burning fuel from the center tank only. That'll leave as much fuel as possible in the outboard wing tanks. The center tank is forward of the CG [center of gravity] and the outboards are aft of CG. Get it?"

"Got it," said Soderlind. "That'll shift the CG rearward. I'm also gonna tell Muldoon to move any passengers he can toward the rear—fill up all the seats they can in the aft section. Now I'd better raise Muldoon."

Northwest can talk to any domestic flight directly from its main base, and Soderlind established radio contact with 227 quickly. He agreed with Muldoon's decision to stay in the New York area while fuel was consumed, and to land at Kennedy where the runways were longer than at Newark.

"Just stay up there until you hear from me again, Harry," the chief pilot said. "We've got a 727 ready for a special test flight. I have a hunch we can work out something that isn't in that Boeing manual—some way to keep that nose off the runway at the lowest practicable speed."

Muldoon explained the situation to his passengers and told the four stewardesses to serve complimentary drinks and dinner. He kept Flight 227 in a holding pattern near Kennedy, where trucks were preparing to foam Runway 22R—the prime purpose of the foam being prevention of sparks from the friction of metal on concrete when the nose touched down. If impact caused any fuel leakage or spray, the tiniest spark could mean fire.

At Minneapolis, meanwhile, Soderlind took off in another 727 with two purposes in mind. First, he wanted to determine as accurately as possible where the nose would touch so the foam could be applied to that portion—there wouldn't be enough to foam the entire runway. Second, he wanted to try out a theory which, if correct, would give Muldoon the lowest possible landing speed in a nose-high roll without any danger of a stall.

His idea involved the precise manipulation of the 727's trailing edge flaps and lift spoilers on the wings—literally hinges that reduce airspeed during the approach and landing phases. The Boeing tri-jet, like nearly all jet transports, has flaps and spoilers that can be "split"—in other words, the so-called hinges located outboard on the wing can be operated independently of those on the inboard area. Normally, flaps and spoilers are operated simultaneously, but in this case, Soderlind figured, splitting would be another way of getting that center of gravity moved back toward the rear.

On the swept-back wing of a jet, the outboard portion of the wing is behind the CG and the inboard portion is ahead. Soderlind's brand-new procedure was to extend only the inboard flaps first—increasing forward lift and thus helping to keep the nose up. Then he planned to extend only the outboard spoilers, which would reduce aft lift and thus tend to keep the tail down.

The tricky part was determining the best moment for splitting. Soderlind found out with relative quickness exactly how the special flap and spoiler management could shift CG rearward without affecting the critical low touchdown speed. He discovered that if he used full flaps and spoilers right up through touchdown, he could achieve minimum safe speed and then activate the special split flap settings just after the main wheels touched.

A single test confirmed Soderlind's experimental procedures. He briefed Muldoon and advised Kennedy Airport exactly where to foam Runway 22R. By this time, Reiman had computed the exact CG shift accomplished by moving passengers and burning fuel off from the center tank. His figures, plus the data from Soderlind's flight test, told the foam and fire truck crews almost to the exact foot where the 727's nose would first touch the runway. The emergency vehicles moved to the recommended area and Muldoon swung Flight 227 into a long approach.

He had already pre-positioned the flap and spoiler emergency controls so the splitting would take place at precisely the right second.

The main wheels touched down about 1,000 feet from the threshold of 22R. About 4,000 feet farther, the nose finally settled into the foam in the predicted spot. The 727 rolled another 600 feet before coming to a gentle stop as the passengers cheered. One man refused to believe that the landing was made with the nose gear retracted until after the occupants evacuated and he could see for himself. Some passengers claimed later it was a smoother landing than they usually experienced.

It *was* smooth, beyond doubt. The only necessary repairs consisted of installing new nose gear doors, adding a tiny patch at the forward end of the nosewheel well and replacing the faulty lock assembly that had caused the trouble.

An official of the Port of New York Authority, which operates Kennedy, informed Northwest that "in all our years of handling various types of emergencies, this was by far the best managed of them all."

There was an important sequel to the incident of Flight 227, however, and one most demonstrative of commercial aviation's cooperative spirit when it comes to safety. Northwest advised Boeing of Soderlind's new technique for landing with a stuck nose gear. Boeing immediately transmitted a full report to all airlines flying 727s.

A few weeks later, a 727 flown by a different carrier had an identical nose gear malfunction. Using the new Northwest procedure, the pilots landed with only superficial damage and no injuries.

4. "THEY BOUGHT
THE FARM . . ."

Let it be said at the outset, firmly and fervently, the jet transport is a brilliantly engineered creation that has demonstrated its inherent safety over the past ten years—against considerable odds and in defiance of pessimistic predictions.

The drama of the jet age has been its very lack of drama. The jetliner literally has wrought a quiet revolution, accomplishing this by getting the public to take for granted not only its speed, comfort, and efficiency but also its ability to provide those three assets with an all-important fourth: safety.

Significantly, the jet—representing the most drastic technical development in commercial aviation history—achieved safety despite an explosive expansion that could well have invited disaster. Between 1963 and 1965, jets flew more hours than they did in their first five years of operations! Considering the fact that the turbine-powered transport was a radically different kind of aircraft, the safety record has been a lot better than many experts believed possible.

In 1967, for example, airlines belonging to the International Civil Aviation Organization (ICAO) compiled their best safety record in history, with .39 passenger fatalities per 100 million passenger miles. Scoff again, if you must, at that maligned mileage yardstick but also consider the fact that this fatality rate was a prodigious 37 percent lower than in 1966 and nearly 30 percent under the previous safest year of 1965. ICAO itself noted that the rate showed signs of flattening out between 1955 and 1960, but then started to drop about 15 percent each year. Inasmuch as the jets began taking over the bulk of worldwide traffic in 1960, the only conclusion is that the jets brought increased safety despite their steadily mounting potential exposure to accident.

We are about to discuss the negative subject of jet crashes, but first it is necessary to examine the positive side of this negative subject. And that is a simple truism: by and large, jets have crashed for basically the same reasons airplanes have always crashed—weather, inadequate ground aids, inferior airport facilities with short runways a prime factor, pilot error, collisions, and sabotage. The overwhelming majority of fatal jet accidents are *not* due directly to the operating characteristics of the jet itself. If anything, those operating characteristics have contributed more to safety than they have detracted from it. To give just one example, the jet is indeed an aircraft that refuses to tolerate human mistakes. This may be a quality representing a potential hazard, yet it also is a quality that breeds discipline and respectful caution in the cockpit to a far greater degree than the pistons ever did.

There is another observation one must make in order to keep jet accidents in a properly focused perspective. The jet age has been comparatively free from those aeronautical engineering gremlins known as "bugs"—major design mistakes that turn up only after airliners enter regular service and which remain perversely hidden through the most rigorous test programs. The jets have had bugs, yes, but not of a calamitous nature, which is no mean attainment considering their greater size and complexity and their different operating environment. The jet was such a revolutionary departure from the pistons that it would not have been surprising to see it spawn some serious design mistakes, as earlier transports did—the Electra, DC-6, Martin 202, Constellation, and Comet, to mention those airliners once afflicted with fatal "bug bites." All but the Electra were grounded for corrective measures, and the latter was forced to operate under severe speed restrictions pending extensive structural modifications.

This is not to say the jets have been totally free of design weaknesses. As with every transport aircraft, they have undergone constant modifications and improvements as the rugged day-by-day rigors of airline operations exposed areas of inadequacy. The 707 or DC-8 in which you fly today is a better airplane than either was at the dawn of the jet age. And two virtues of the jetliner have exceeded the rosiest hopes of engineers, both involving safety. One is structural integrity. The other is engine reliability.

The jet's brute strength has been described previously— in those two instances in which jets lost part of their wings and still remained flyable. After the second incident, the TWA-Eastern collision, some unknown wag sent a message over TWA's teletype system amending the airline's "no go" list—those items which *must* be in perfect condition before an aircraft is allowed to move one inch from a ramp. The tongue-in-cheek order, transmitted to all TWA stations, read:

AMENDMENT TO INOPERATIVE EQUIPMENT LIST — EFFECTIVE IMMEDIATELY — ALL BOEING 707S MAY BE DISPATCHED WITH RGHT OR LEFT WING MISSING.

The reliability record of the turbine engine is best illustrated with a single comparison. In 1959, the FAA required jet power plants to be overhauled after only 1,000 hours of operation: in some cases, the overhaul time was 800 hours. In 1968, most turbine engines were going 6,000-8,000 hours between overhauls, and even this is conservative. Many power plant experts believe a jet engine, properly maintained and inspected regularly, could go on almost indefinitely without needing a major tear-down. The FAA has even begun allowing some airlines to eliminate major overhauls if they follow a new system of replacing certain components at regular intervals.

If the designers deserve unstinted praise for what they achieved in strength and reliability, however, they also warrant a spanking for their occasional transgressions. The airlines have felt for years that airframe manufacturers, operating under federal certification requirements, perform admirably in meeting or even surpassing those stiff requirements but occasionally are less diligent in areas where there are no certification standards.

The certification process for the commercial transport itself deserves an explanation. FAA engineers work with factory technicians almost from the start of the first blueprints for a new airliner. The FAA specialists lay down certain specifications and tests which the final product must meet. Can the plane, for example, suffer engine failure while taking off with a full load on a hot summer day from an airport considerably above sea level and still climb safely? Are key structural parts stressed to withstand sudden jolts or prolonged gust forces? Does cockpit visibility come up to minimum standards? Are there adequate backup systems for any control component that might fail?

Certification has played an underrated role in air safety; the rare failures stemming from inadequate certification have obscured the many times the process has nipped bugs before an airplane began carrying passengers. But there are weaknesses and drawbacks, starting with the fact that the FAA lacks the funds for hiring sufficient technical experts (thanks to the Budget Bureau and Congress, the latter a highly vocal demander of greater air safety while it simultaneously and with alarming frequency cuts air safety appropriations). With limited engineering personnel, the FAA delegates some portion of its certification duties to the manufacturers, who, in turn, assign trusted employees to the program.

This delegation of authority has resulted in certification of at least 4 airliners with fatal bugs—the Constellation, the DC-6, the Martin 202, and the Electra. All four were certificated despite weaknesses which resulted in serious accidents. The Constellation had an electrical wiring flaw which led to a fatal in-flight fire. The DC-6 had an air scoop which sucked overflow fuel from wing tanks into the heating system ducts. The Martin 202 was built with a key structural part in the wings made of an untested alloy, one which developed metal fatigue in a short time. The Electra's well-publicized troubles stemmed from a susceptibility to a kind of vibration that led to catastrophic wing failure.

Certification work by factory engineers has been vastly improved since the jets, and the liaison between FAA and manufacturers also is far closer than it was in the past. Also significant is the fact that the airframe manufacturers do, indeed, impose on their new planes tougher test programs than FAA requires.

But limited FAA manpower, nevertheless, has resulted in limited certification. Robert E. Stone, United's Director of Flight Safety and an ex-line pilot, told an ALPA safety forum that "one of the greatest faults of certification is that it concentrates on the 'killer items.'" By this, he meant that certification—with its numerically inadequate personnel—must focus on major items most directly concerned with safety.

"This is fine," Stone added, "for we get an airplane that is basically safe, but the little detail items are not covered by adequate certification rules and these drive us crazy."

The UAL official went on to cite such examples as a cabin lighting system that somehow managed to garble navigation and communication signals, or a cockpit voice recorder whose tape kept jamming. Stone said United actually found it could purchase CO_2 cartridges in a liquor store which were better than those a safety equipment manufacturer was supplying for the airline's life jackets. United, he said, once bought new altimeters which supposedly would correct themselves for temperature and airspeed variations by means of an electro-servo unit. In actual flight experience, the servos not only didn't work but also made the altimeters more dangerous. UAL has a "top twenty" list showing the 20 aircraft parts that fail most frequently. Stone said that for the first three months of 1966, 19 of the items on the "top twenty" list for the DC-8 were not covered by certification. The same ratio was true for the Boeing 720.

Every airliner has certain "no go" components—meaning that if a "no go" item is inoperative, the airplane cannot fly until repairs are made. According to Stone, 6 of the uncertificated items on the DC-8's "top 20" were of the "no go" variety, and there were 8 such uncertificated items on the Boeing 720 list.

("The FAA," an airline official once remarked to me more in sadness than bitterness, "would certificate an outhouse if the crescent was shaped right.")

As Stone himself pointed out, certification has made massive contributions to air safety and the manufacturers' insistence on going beyond certification standards has made almost as many. Yet with the ever increasing complexity of airliners, disaster needs only a sliver of an opening through which to strike—a jet crash on March 1, 1962, offered stark evidence of this.

It was an American Airlines 707 that left New York for Los Angeles with 8 crew members and 87 passengers. Only eight seconds after takeoff, the plane lurched to the left, banked sharply and continued an almost graceful roll until it was on its back. Then it fell, nose down, into the shallow waters of Jamaica Bay. There were no survivors.

The CAB's report, announced ten months later, found that: ". . . the probable cause of this accident was a rudder control system malfunction producing yaw, sideslip and roll leading to a loss of control from which recovery action was not effective."

Boiled down to layman phraseology, the CAB findings determined that a short circuit had occurred in the wiring of a small motor which activates the hydraulic boost system for the rudder. It might be compared to what would happen if the power steering on an automobile suddenly jammed while the wheel was in a sharp turn. In the case of the American 707, according to the CAB, the electrical malfunction resulted in crossed wires, sending the wrong voltage through the circuits and giving the rudder an unwanted hard-over signal that took the pilots by surprise.

The rudder servo unit from the wrecked plane was recovered and examined. Investigators found evidence of pre-impact damage on the wires—scratches, punctures, and other unexplainable gouge marks. CAB experts visited the factory where the units were manufactured and watched the assembly process. One investigator noticed a pair of tweezers on a bench and asked the workman what they were used for. The workman explained that he needed the tweezers to grasp a cord which had to be wrapped around the wires. The investigator examined several units that had just come off the assembly line—units on which tweezers had been used—and found damage identical to what had been discovered on the little motor from the American 707.

The CAB's verdict has been disputed by Boeing, American, and the FAA. The latter still believes the crash resulted from a wrongly installed bolt (put in upside down by mistake) which fell out of the hydraulic system, rammed excess fluid into one side of the rudder control system, and caused a sudden, violent shove that locked the controls while the plane was in a turn. If true, this FAA analysis was just one more manifestation of "Murphy's Law"—namely, "if an aircraft part can be installed incorrectly, someone will install it that way." At least two major crashes in the United States, and several more overseas, have been blamed on application of "Murphy's Law."

The doubts raised against the CAB's verdict in the Jamaica Bay accident were based largely on flight tests which duplicated the rudder control malfunction alleged by the Board. Boeing and the FAA maintained that a short circuit in the servo unit would have resulted in comparatively little force, which, even if totally unexpected, could have been easily overridden by the pilots. Boeing, in fact, deliberately short-circuited the unit without warning on several test flights. The pilots had no difficulty in maintaining control and stopping the roll. As far as Boeing is concerned, the crash is still unexplained—no other jet has had any experience which might throw some new light on what happened over Jamaica Bay. Many pilots bitterly point out that whatever control malfunction occurred, it came when the American flight was just starting a noise abatement turn at low altitude, with insufficient room for recovery. It would be hard to convince pilots that noise abatement didn't play a role in this accident.

We may never know whether a short circuit in wires no longer than a pencil and only one sixth of an inch thick was responsible for 95 deaths, or whether the cause was a one-inch bolt costing about twenty-five cents. But in either case, the lesson to be learned is identical. A jet carries more than 3,000 pounds of safety, standby, and emergency installations. Its navigation and communications equipment alone costs more than an entire transport did twenty years ago. Yet safety, or death, may hinge on such seemingly insignificant items as the thread design on a tiny bolt or the innocent use of tweezers on a few little wires. The true tragedy of the American crash was that catastrophe in the form of a ridiculously tiny Achilles' heel managed to defeat all the previous efforts made to assure the maximum of safety.

Commercial aviation history is replete with such examples, although frequency of occurrence has lessened in the age of the more ruthlessly tested jets. Yet the jets, as just shown, are not immune from the ravages of these tiny but deadly gremlins.

Take the case of United Flight 266, a Boeing 727, which crashed shortly after taking off from Los Angeles International Airport for Denver on January 18, 1969. Two minutes after the aircraft broke ground, the pilot radioed that he had a fire warning on number one engine and was shutting it down. As a precautionary measure, he decided to return to the airport but he never made it. The

117

target that was Flight 266 disappeared from the radar screen as the jet made a left turn from its departure heading. There were no survivors.

The wreckage was located in about 1,000 feet of water, through the use of sonar and underwater television cameras. Much of it was recovered by a new research submarine developed by Lockheed. It already had proved its value by recovering the flight recorder of an SAS DC-8 that had crashed in the same area only five days before Flight 266 plunged into the Pacific.

At this writing, no report has been issued on the UAL crash but investigators already are pretty certain of the cause—total electrical failure that probably was inadvertent or accidental rather than an actual malfunction.

The flight was dispatched with one of its three generators inoperative—on number three engine. This was perfectly legal; operating a 727 with only two generators is considered completely safe and, in fact, a faulty generator is listed as merely a deferred item on the minimum equipment list which means repair or replacement could await the completion of the trip.

But the generators are responsible for supplying electrical power, including power sources for many instruments, cockpit lighting, and the electrically operated trim tab and flap controls. When the captain shut down number one engine because of the fire warning (it was a false warning, examination of the recovered engine disclosed later), he was left with only the generator on number two engine supplying electrical power. One theory is that the lone remaining generator was overloaded, causing total failure. But the evidence is against this because the overload would have to be massive; engineers are convinced that if unnecessary power was reduced, the one generator should have been able to handle the minimum load required for vital instruments and controls.

Why didn't it? Speculation and investigation has centered around two possibilities:

1. When the false fire warning sounded and the number one engine was shut down, emergency procedures required the flight engineer to reduce the load on the remaining generators. This would have been accomplished by cutting secondary power outlets *including the galley power*. But on the 727, the galley power switch is located above the battery switch and is out of the FE's line of sight. It is very

possible that the FE mistakenly hit the battery switch, which would have knocked out all power, instead of the galley switch. (Interestingly enough, all 727 operators have now installed a guard over the battery switch to prevent inadvertent or accidental triggering.)

2. This was a 727 QC, a model which has the main battery switch located in precisely the same spot as a cooling fan switch on standard 727s. The FE had plenty of experience in the latter aircraft but only 20 hours on the 727 QC. Under the pressure of an emergency, did he instinctively pull the battery switch instead of the one that normally activates fans for the air-conditioning system during the lower speeds of takeoffs and climbs? The fan switch is on the checklist for reducing unessential power.

All this is conjecture, but theoretical reconstruction seems logical.

The captain, alerted by the fire warning, tells the FE to reduce the power load and simultaneously shuts down number one engine. The FE hits the battery switch accidentally, either mistaking it for the galley power or fan switch. The single operating generator is subjected to overload and a circuit breaker trips it—leaving everything in total darkness.

The crew now has no lights, no electricity, no electric trim tab control, no radio, no instruments, and no visual references outside—the jet is over the water at night, in rain. All this occurs in the middle of a critical return-to-airport maneuver. Just the lack of trim tab control is extremely hazardous, for the aircraft's center of gravity changes during a climb or descent.

The captain is now forced into the impossible position of flying by instinct, literally a "seat-of-the-pants" situation, and under these conditions luck more than skill is needed. He runs out of luck and altitude almost at the same moment and flies the plane into the water. All aboard are killed—6 crew members and 32 passengers, the latter including a number of UAL pilots flying to Denver for 727 training which was a touch of final irony. (10)

Again, this is theory but reasonable theory and an excellent demonstration of what we have discussed earlier: the anatomy of most accidents consisting of a series of chain reactions instead of a single cause, and the guilt of a comparatively minor component undermining hundreds of safety devices and precautions—in the case of Flight 266, perhaps, the location of a small switch in an otherwise superbly designed cockpit.

Or, in another instance, a tiny, apparently insignificant valve.

On June 23, 1967, a black-and-gold Mohawk BAC-111 took off from Elmira, N.Y., bound for Washington, D.C. Flight 40 was observed by a number of ground witnesses to be trailing smoke and fire at an unusually low altitude. Several saw the tail section separate from the aircraft which then nosed over and dove to earth. There were 2 pilots, 2 stewardesses, and 30 passengers aboard. All were killed. The weather at the time was perfect; the time of the crash was fixed as shortly before 2:50 P.M.

Investigators found early evidence of a fire in the tail that burned through radio wires and eventually the elevator controls. The cockpit voice recorder also gave them a grim picture of a crew hit by a mysterious emergency for which there was no explanation and therefore no procedures for combating it.

The first indication of trouble came as Air Traffic Control was clearing the flight to climb to 16,000 feet and just after the crew advised ATC they were on their way to 6,000. The recorder tape contained a brief, earthy expletive from the captain.

The copilot, who apparently was flying the two-engine, British-made jetliner, answered:

"It's hard to tell what it is."

Eight seconds later, the captain told the first officer to "pull back on your speed."

"I'm doing it," the latter replied.

The tape then showed that the captain took over the controls and decided to return to Elmira. He so advised ATC but the New York Center, handling the flight, never heard him. Five minutes before the crash, the captain suddenly exclaimed, "We lost all control . . . we don't have anything."

F/O: "We're in manual now."

Captain: "Yeah, but I can't do anything."

The tape then recorded the sound of the landing gear warning horn. It ceased momentarily, then started up again.

Captain: "Put it back in the second system."

A pause of thirteen seconds. The captain said they'd better "go up for a minute." For the next thirty to thirty-five seconds, there was frantic dialogue involving attempts to control the plane.

"Pull back! Pull back! . . . keep working, we're making it . . . straight now . . . climb now . . . easy now . . . now, cut the gun . . . we're in now."

The landing gear horn went off.

There was some brief, momentary debate on whether to head for Elmira; apparently, in the confusion of an unexplainable control problem, the crew had been concentrating on solving this before going back.

At 2:46 P.M., the captain decided, "Let's go straight ahead." Seconds later, he asked rather desperately:

"What have we done to that . . . tail surface—ya have any idea?"

"I don't know," the first officer said. "I just can't figure it out . . . we've lost both systems."

Captain: "I can't keep this (aircraft) from . . . all right, I'm gonna use both hands now."

There then came a series of remarks which referred to using "both hands" and "pulling back."

At 2:47 P.M., the captain's voice came through loud and clear.

"I've gone out of control."

The recording ended six seconds later.

The source of their fatal dilemma was traced to a small, spring-loaded valve in the Auxiliary Power Unit (APU), the latter a motor which supplies power to various components both in flight and on the ground. The APU, for example, powers the main staircase door at the front of the plane and runs the air-conditioning system on the ground without the necessity of hooking up the aircraft to a ground truck. In flight, as a supplementary power source, the APU utilizes some of the bleed air from the engines as a supplementary source of power. The valve in question, called a nonreturn valve, was designed to keep the hot air from getting back into the chamber housing the APU.

The nonreturn valve on Flight 40 failed to close, allowing air heated to nearly 400 degrees Centigrade to flow back toward the APU. The temperature was sufficiently high to self-ignite acoustic linings that had been contaminated with flammable hydraulic fluid. This fluid that had leaked into the linings was partially decomposed and thus was more rapidly ignited than fresh fluid could have been. The result was a fire in an area lacking fire protection (no

121

one could imagine the circumstances that caused this combustion as even a remote possibility), one that spread rapidly and eventually destroyed the structural integrity of the hydraulic lines, rudder fittings, and fin spars.

The British Aircraft Corporation, maker of the BAC-111, took swift corrective action based on recommendations of the NTSB and subsequent mandatory orders of the FAA. A fireproof barrier was installed between the vertical tail fin and the rear bay containing hydraulic lines, electrical circuits, and control components. An aluminum alloy wall separating this bay from the APU chamber was replaced with fireproofed stainless steel. The acoustic linings in the chamber were removed, and the nonreturn valve was made bigger and stronger. All airlines operating the BAC-111 agreed to ban use of the APU in flight until the foregoing modifications were completed. And finally, most of these improvements also were incorporated in other jets including addition of an APU fire sensor device.

The loophole was closed—too late to save the lives of 36 persons, but in time to protect the lives of the millions who will fly the BAC-111 in the future.

The aviation industry *is* learning the lessons taught by disaster. And one such lesson is the greater extent to which new planes are being tested before they fly passengers. This is not to say transports like the DC-8 and 707 were inadequately tested; they underwent what were at the time the most ruthless, extensive test programs in history. But it is an aviation rule that daily airline flying sometimes can uncover bugs which defy exposure by the toughest test flying.

In the early part of the jet age, the new transports were plagued by a wave of hydraulic failures—first in the 707 and later in the DC-8. There were an alarming number of incidents in which landing gears refused to come down normally—sufficient to warrant frantic grounding demands by several Congressmen who did not take time to consider the fact that a stuck landing gear had yet to kill a single passenger.

The public, which deserves credit for not getting as hysterical as certain lawmakers, nevertheless must have wondered why jets came up with hydraulic difficulties after supposedly thorough test programs. And there must have been some concern generated by the statements coming from a few Congressmen who, as is so often the case, leaped before they looked. Not one who pressured the FAA to ground first the 707 and later the DC-8 took the trouble to ask for a briefing on what was causing the technical problems. And the cause was not only simple but symptomatic of the teething pains suffered by most new airliners that are bigger and more complex than their predecessors.

First, the jet's hydraulic system is ten times more complicated than corresponding equipment on pistons. In addition to greater complexity, the system is subjected to drastic temperature changes which can literally "age" some of the components. Some parts have worn out before expected. A jet can take off with the ground thermometers reading 100 degrees and in a few minutes be cruising at 35,000 feet in outside temperatures of 20 degrees below zero. Older, prop-driven aircraft at one time had fewer gear problems because their hydraulic systems had benefited from years of refinement. Gear failures on the jets are diminishing, too, for the same reason—improvements resulting from experience and better maintenance.

An FAA-industry campaign to cure the gear difficulties in the early jet years was typical.

The FAA and the airlines agreed on nine modifications to the DC-8 hydraulic system and generally similar changes in that of the Boeing. The airlines also instituted stricter inspection and maintenance procedures as well as checking flight crews to make sure they were following prescribed procedures for dealing with hydraulic emergencies. The airlines began filing faster, more frequent, and detailed reports on every conceivable type of hydraulic malfunction, no matter how minor.

This enabled the FAA and the industry to prevent insignificant problems from developing into major ones.

In less than seven months, the concerted government-airline effort reduced hydraulic incidents from a peak of 16 per 1,000 hours of flight to 5 per 1,000 hours. The rate today is down to the level or even below that of piston-engine aircraft.

Admittedly, this is no comfort to a passenger at best inconvenienced and at worst frightened when an airliner encounters an abnormal situation, such as a jammed gear. But it is the purpose of this book to emphasize the positive while acknowledging the negative. For every so-called abnormal situation or even real emergency, there are about

1½ million completely routine flights. And this, too, must be realized when anyone looks askance at the weaknesses in scheduled air transportation.

Yes, we are examining jet crashes—their causes and their cures. It is not particularly pleasant reading; it may frighten some readers and it could bring pain to anyone who has lost a loved one or friend in an air crash. But it should not bring indignation, anger, or doubts toward a U.S. manufacturing industry that has produced three out of every four commercial transports flying the world's airlines, or a U.S. airline industry that lands approximately 85 percent of its 8 million annual flights within fifteen minutes or less of scheduled arrival times and completes more than 97 percent of its scheduled mileage. For every tragedy, there are hundreds of thousands of triumphs, and that is precisely what a safely completed flight is—a triumph forged by skill, responsibility, and devotion to the goal of constant safety improvement.

Pilots have a pet expression for fatal accidents—the typically casual jargon of the airman who feels emotion deeply but tries so hard to hide those emotions under a blanket of half cynicism, half fatalism.

"They bought the farm" is the way they refer to a crash.*

Captain Roy W. Almquist, like many veteran airline pilots, flew for a living but had an avocation to which he devoted most of his off-duty time. Based in Minneapolis, he also was a banker, president of his local Lions Club, and definitely a solid citizen.

On February 12, 1963, Roy Almquist was commanding Northwest Flight 705, nonstop from Miami to Chicago. He took off on schedule, at 1:30 P.M. Approximately twenty minutes later, Almquist and the rest of the 43 persons aboard Flight 705 were dead and the wreckage of their Boeing 720B was scattered over a wide area of the Florida Everglades. For the first time since the dawn of the jet age, a U.S. jetliner had disintegrated in the air.

That one aspect shook the entire aviation industry. There already had been reassuring evidence that the jets were stronger than their designers had planned. A Pan Am 707, only a few months after the start of jet service, had

---

* The term is believed to stem from the days when barnstorming flyers and airmail pilots made forced landings on farms and had to pay for any damage done to fields or crops.

gone into an unexpected dive from 35,000 feet over the Atlantic. By the time control was regained (the autopilot had inadvertently disengaged), the plane had plunged to 6,000 feet, exceeding the speed of sound. It later was determined that during the dive, the 707 had been subjected to load forces nearly six times the force of gravity, *exceeding the design limits established by Boeing engineers by a sizable margin*. The G forces were so great that when the captain landed, both his eyes were blackened as if by heavy blows.

It was a hair-raising yet comforting incident, for it showed that the strength of a battleship had been put into the jet's aluminum skeleton and skin. More than four years of safe jet operations transpired between the Pan Am dive and the destruction of Northwest Flight 705. There had been accidents, but none involving supposedly impossible structural failure.

Yet it was obvious that the NWA 720B *had* suffered structural disintegration, and in the violent turbulence of a thunderstorm. This was a fate not unknown to piston-engine planes, but no one thought it likely that a storm could tear apart a mighty jet. There seemed to be no doubt that turbulence was involved. The record of communications between Flight 705 and Miami Departure Control contained frequent references to severe turbulence and repeated requests from 705 for vectoring out of the storm in the vicinity of Miami International Airport.

At one point, Flight 705's copilot—Robert Feller—advised Departure Control:

"Ah, we're in the clear now. We can see it out ahead . . . looks pretty bad."

"It" was the boiling caldron of a thunderhead, containing storm cells of near-tornadic strength.

Departure Control, rather apologetically, assured Feller it had vectored Flight 705 into what ground radar showed was the least turbulent area. It cleared the flight to climb to its assigned cruising altitude of 25,000 feet.

"Okay," Feller replied. "Ah . . . we'll make a left turn about thirty degrees here and climb."

"Is two-seven-oh your climb-out heading?" Departure Control asked.

"Affirmative," said Feller. "It'll take us out in the open again."

Departure Control gave 705 permission to turn to a

heading of 270 degrees and climb, even as Feller reported that the turbulence was moderate to heavy. Again, Departure Control assured him that the vectoring course was intended to avoid the worst turbulence and at the same time steer clear of conflicting traffic, the later getting obvious priority.

"Okay," Feller said with a trace of sarcasm. "You'd better run the rest of them off the other way, then."

(When the CAB studied the transmission tape later, it was apparent there had been a persistent conflict between Flight 705 and Departure Control—the crew kept complaining that the vectoring courses were exposing the flight to a bad pounding, and the controller working 705 kept insisting, in effect, that he was doing the best he could, considering the demands of other traffic. This "conflict of interest" occurs too often. The CAB report on the accident noted that: "Clearly, both were seeking the safest, most expeditious route. The misunderstanding resulted from the pilot's desire to avoid the squall line and the controller's prime responsibility to provide adequate separation from known IFR traffic." Pilots wish the FAA had sufficient funds for dual radar installations, one to monitor weather and the other for monitoring traffic, as well as additional personnel to handle such equipment.)

The last communication from 705 was Feller's laconic, "We're just about out of seventeen-five [seventeen thousand, five hundred feet] . . ."

The time was 1:48 P.M.

Less than two minutes later, ground witnesses saw an orange ball of flame flare up amid the black thunderclouds, then fall to the ground.

Not until June 4, 1965, did the Civil Aeronautics Board release its findings on the destruction of Flight 705. Twenty-seven months is an unusually long period between the occurrence of an accident and the issuance of a "probable cause" report. But the solution of Flight 705's death involved some of the most vital safety research in aviation history, for it exposed hitherto unsuspected hazards in the jet's operating characteristics. Incredible as it may seem, the hazards were not detected in the hundreds of flight test hours or thousands of airline flight hours accumulated before the Northwest accident.

Jets had been tossed about by severe turbulence many times—prior to February 12, 1963, there were 34 incidents in which passengers were injured and/or jet transports damaged—but not until Flight 705 was wrenched apart did the phrase "turbulence upset" take on a new and deadly meaning. And the delayed recognition of this upset problem can only be interpreted as a combination of lack of experience with serious loss of control during turbulence, and the unhappy fact that it took a fatal crash to focus attention on the upset phenomenon.

To understand Flight 705's fate and subsequent upset incidents, both fatal and nonfatal, it is necessary to reconstruct what must have occurred in the cockpit when an emergency confronted Captain Almquist and First Officer Feller with which they were not prepared to deal—and through no real fault of their own, or of anyone else, for that matter.

They were climbing to their assigned altitude, still being punched around by turbulence, when their 720B slammed into massive updrafts. The nose of the aircraft tilted up sharply and airspeed dropped accordingly—down to the point where Almquist, flying the plane, became alarmed at the possibility of a stall. He reacted as almost any pilot would have at the time. He pressed his left thumb on a small button attached to the control yoke. This is the electrical stabilizer trim switch—known to Boeing pilots as the "pickle switch." This switch is hooked to a small electric motor in the tail section. When the black button is pressed, the motor manipulates the entire horizontal stabilizer.

On ordinary planes, the horizontal stabilizers are fixed, with only the elevators—the hinges attached to the rear of the stabilizers—able to move up or down, providing what is known as longitudinal control: the means of climbing or descending. But on jets, it is possible to move the whole stabilizer area. (David Hoffman of the Washington *Post* gave the best analogy of this function when he compared it to a child sticking his hand out of a car window, adjusting or trimming "the angle of his fingertips to porpoise his palm in the windstream outside a moving car.")

Almquist was faced with an abnormally out-of-trim condition—nose up and airspeed evaporating. He pushed the "pickle switch" forward and shoved his yoke forward at the same time. The jet dove, but simultaneously—as the flight recorder showed later—Flight 705 suddenly was caught in the vicious vise of a huge downdraft. With all controls literally locked in a dive position, the jet accelerated sickeningly and rapidly. The CAB's report describes what must have been taking place in the cockpit during these few terrible seconds:

"Besides the distraction of warning lights and ringing bells which were probably actuated under the negative G conditions, loose items such as briefcases, charts, logbooks, etc., would be tossed around. The crew members themselves would be forced upward against their belts and the average airline pilot would probably have difficulty keeping his feet on the rudder pedals and his hands on the control wheel."

It probably took Almquist eight seconds before he managed to get his hands back on the control yoke. In those eight seconds, Flight 705 went into a vertical dive exceeding 500 miles an hour and with airspeed increasing steadily. He hauled back on the yoke. The nose stayed down. The dive continued. He continued to apply back pressure in a desperate tug-of-war against the aerodynamic loads building up on the stabilizers and elevators. It was no contest. The tug-of-war ended when the loads exceeded the design strength of the stabilizer-elevator section. The elevators snapped off and Flight 705 plunged helplessly toward the swamps below. As the uncontrollable dive rose to almost supersonic speeds the jet began to spin, engine pods and wings broke off, and fuel tanks exploded.

Recall the experience of Captain Duescher (Chapter 3). He was challenged by the same emergency as Almquist. He came through because he resisted the temptation to recover control until his own 720 was at a lower altitude where elevator response was possible. This is not to blame Almquist. He was relatively inexperienced in jets—of his nearly 18,000 hours of flight time, only 150 hours were in the 720. Copilot Feller, with more than 1,000 hours in Boeing jets, presented the unusual situation of a first officer being more experienced than his captain in this particular type of aircraft. Almquist was no stranger to thunderstorm turbulence—not with more than 17,000 hours logged—but he *was* a stranger to the effects of turbulence on swept-wing aircraft. (11)

Those effects became only too apparent after the Northwest crash, the Duescher incident, several other instances of temporary control loss during severe turbulence, and finally some hard-nose research performed by Boeing,

Douglas, NASA, and airline flight superintendents. Paul Soderlind of Northwest, who had been a close friend of Almquist, embarked on what amounted to an educational crusade. He wrote probably the most widely distributed safety publication of all time—a discourse on jet behavior during turbulence and ways to combat it. He also toured the country, addressing pilot groups of all airlines.

Literally, Soderlind recommended an entirely different approach. Previous to the Northwest crash, jet pilots had been penetrating storm areas in the same manner in which they had flown straight-wing aircraft into known rough air —slowing down to specified speeds to prevent structural damage. As far as the jets were concerned, there were two dangers in following the old procedure: (1) the jets were being slowed down too much, creating the possibility of stalls, and (2) pilots were trying too hard to maintain airspeed during severe updrafts and downdrafts, instead of concentrating on keeping their aircraft level.

Soderlind's advice, supported by industry and government flight and wind tunnel tests, was to increase turbulence penetration speeds slightly—he reasoned that the jets were structurally capable of withstanding the greater stresses generated by the higher penetration speeds, and that preventing stalls was more important. Second, he urged pilots snared by severe turbulence not to worry so much about such pressure instruments as airspeed indicators. He reminded his fellow airmen that in turbulence those instruments often are unreadable anyway, and that trying to "chase" them can lead to loss of control. He also warned against actuating the electrical trim switch during turbulence, but to rely instead on manual control of the elevators and, above all, to concentrate on maintaining level attitude—in other words, he was telling them to let the jets almost fly themselves through storms, instead of fighting turbulence. Similar and equally important missionary work was done by Frank Kolk of American Airlines.

Inability to read instruments when an aircraft is being flipped around in a storm has been an aviation problem for a long time. It is a more serious problem with jets because the swept-wing aircraft loses lift more rapidly in violently rough air and correspondingly rapid attitude changes. Because most instruments operate via the pressure of air forced to the instruments by aircraft movement, such attitude changes can result in erratic instrument readings. Airspeed, for example, can fluctuate more than 200 miles an hour in turbulence as aircraft attitude itself fluctuates. An Eastern DC-8 captain, whose plane was almost rolled on its back in a thunderstorm shortly after taking off from Dulles International Airport, described what can happen during severe turbulence in succinct terms.

"We encountered the most violent jolt I have ever experienced in over twenty thousand hours of flying. I felt as though an extremely severe positive, upward acceleration had triggered off a buffeting, not a pitch, that increased in frequency and magnitude as one might expect to encounter sitting on the end of a huge tuning fork that had been struck violently. Not an instrument on any panel was readable to its full scale but appeared as a white blur against its dark background. From that point on—it could have been ten, twenty, sixty or a hundred seconds—we had no idea of attitude, altitude, airspeed, or heading. We were now on instruments with no visual reference and continued with severe to violent buffeting, ripping, tearing, rending, crashing sounds. Briefcases, manuals, ashtrays, suitcases, pencils, cigarettes, flashlights were flying about like unguided missiles. It sounded and felt as if pods were leaving and the structure disintegrating. The objects that were thrashing about the cockpit seemed momentarily to settle on the ceiling, which made it impossible to trust one's senses, although I had a feeling that we were inverted as my seat belt was tight and had stretched considerably. As my briefcase was on the ceiling, I looked up and through the overhead window and felt that I was looking down on the top of a cloud deck. The first officer said later he had the same impression at the same instant, as we acted in unison, applying as much force as we could gather to roll aileron control to the left. The [artificial] horizon bar at this time started to stabilize and showed us coming back through ninety degrees vertical to a level attitude laterally. At this time, I had my first airspeed reading, decaying through two hundred and fifty knots. The air smoothed out and we gently leveled off at between fourteen hundred and fifteen hundred feet . . ."

That vivid account explains why the airline pilot's traditional recommended maneuver for combating a thunderstorm is a 180-degree turn. It also underlines the propensity of some jet instruments to go into a frenetic dance during a turbulence upset. Of particular concern is the artificial horizon indicator; large transports are not flown by the old "seat-of-the-pants" feeling and jets are even more reliant on instrument flying than are pistons. The artificial horizon indicator tells a pilot when he is flying level, climbing or descending, and in many of the most serious turbulence cases studied during the "trouble with turbulence" years, crews lost their only attitude references when their horizon indicators went crazy. Inability to "feel" aircraft attitude is particularly hazardous at night or in an overcast.

The new technique of giving attitude a priority over airspeed was a major step in preventing upsets from occurring in the first place; the old reverse priority, airspeed over attitude, resulted in haywire instruments and loss of control before pilots could do anything about maintaining attitude. A second safety bonus was added when the airlines adopted new artificial horizon indicators which are far easier to read and less prone to tumble. And most important, pilot training and retraining have emphasized the new procedures exerting more moderate control forces when counteracting turbulence instead of fighting it.

Significantly, turbulence upset instances have diminished since mid-1964 when the research, better instrumentation, and new techniques began to pay off. Jets still run into jarring air—one can no more eliminate turbulence itself than repeal the law of gravity—but not with the resultant loss of control that plagued the industry in the early sixties. It is quite natural, however, for the public to ask why the turbulence problem seemed to catch the airlines by surprise. The crash of Northwest Flight 705 occurred four and a half years after the start of U.S. commercial jet service, and while there had been no fatal accidents attributed to turbulence, there had been more than 30 serious incidents—presumably sufficient advance warning that a pattern and a problem existed.

The answer is that no one recognized the pattern until lives were lost, a situation which seems to be one of the less praiseworthy aspects of air safety progress. This is not to imply that the industry and the government always wait for a fatal crash before action is taken. The opposite is true. The FAA issues "airworthiness directives" almost daily. These are mandatory corrective orders based on the constant flow of reports coming into the agency from the airlines. These reports are watched closely for the slightest sign of a developing pattern that could affect safety. Repeated or persistent malfunctions involving a certain component on a certain type airplane, for example, will bring a telegraphed warning to all carriers operating that kind of aircraft, along with a "fix" order to be accomplished by a certain deadline—sometimes before the plane is allowed to fly again. Frequently, the aircraft and/or engine manufacturers will wire the airlines advising them to inspect, repair, or replace components which seem suspect. So widespread and rapid is this sharing of operational experience that the FAA's airworthiness directives often are mere confirmations of what the airlines already have done on the advice of the manufacturers.

In the case of the upset problem, there unquestionably was an element of overconfidence in the jet itself—specifically in its structural brawn. Airplanes had been endangered by turbulence since the beginning of aviation. Airliners had been wrecked by angry storms long before the jets came along. In the pre-jet years, the test flights failed to disclose any particular handling difficulties in rough air that were not true of straight-wing aircraft—that was the reason jet storm-penetration speeds were proportionately the same as those of the older transports.

The Northwest accident that opened an aeronautical Pandora's box officially was blamed primarily on Boeing and to a lesser extent on the airline. Two years after the crash, a Chicago jury ordered Boeing to pay $1.6 million to the widow of one of the victims, and Northwest was found liable for another $400,000 in damages. The widow's attorneys convinced the jury that the 720's horizontal stabilizers were defective and that Boeing waited until after the accident to warn pilots that turbulence techniques should be changed.

Without casting aspersions on any collection of "tried and true" jurists, their verdict was technically unsound. Boeing had no monopoly on the instability of jets in rough air under certain circumstances, any more than its planes had a monopoly on rugged construction. All swept-wing aircraft were subject to turbulence hazards, not because of design weaknesses but because it was not known at the time that they had to be flown differently. True, the certification process failed to go into this sufficiently.

(It does now. The DC-9 and Boeing 737 were required

to fly through severe thunderstorms as part of their certification tests, and those tests included instrument behavior during deliberately induced upsets. The new jets were not only tested for their handling characteristics in severe turbulence but they were even exposed to a fully untrimmed condition—their horizontal stabilizers were positioned full up or full down, and the aircraft then were rolled and dived to make sure pilots could recover safely.)

When the Boeings were having some early upset problems, many DC-8 captains rather complacently decided they were fortunate to be flying what they considered a more stable airplane. In a sense, the DC-8 is somewhat easier to handle than the 707 because its wings are swept back at a slightly lesser angle. Some pilots who have flown both planes claim the DC-8 flies more like a conventional airplane and is more docile than the Boeing. But any complacency on the part of the DC-8 crews was eradicated quickly.

An Eastern Air Lines DC-8 brushed its wing tips against disaster on November 9, 1963, while flying from Houston to Mexico City. Shortly after departing from Houston, it flew into a thunderstorm. The commanding pilot, Mel French, asked Air Traffic Control for a course change because his airborne radar showed turbulence ahead. Copilot Grant Newby was flying the plane and French was still discussing (arguing would be a better word) a different heading with the controller when the DC-8 went into a roller coaster ride—updrafts and then downdrafts of severe and prolonged duration. The horizon indicator might as well have been the "tilt" sign of a pinball machine; it was useless. The jet suddenly dipped into a high-speed dive from just under 6,000 feet.

Both pilots tried to pull out, but the control yokes seemed to be riveted in a forward position. Their airspeed, the flight recorder showed later, was more than 600 miles an hour. They were too close to the ground to bring the nose up by increasing power, as Duescher had done three months before. French had only one recourse and he acted with skill and masterful speed. He reversed thrust on all four engines. He couldn't have done this on a Boeing, whose reverse thrust can be used only on the ground for braking power. But on the DC-8 two of the four engines can be reversed in flight as a kind of auxiliary aerial brake. French's application of reverse thrust slowed the plunging

133

jet just enough for the pilots to regain some elevator control. Their yokes came back, slowly and grudgingly. They managed to get the jet level at around 2,000 feet, but this lifesaving maneuver generated enough stress to tear off the number three engine pod and damage a second pod.

French made an emergency landing at Barksdale Air Force Base, outside of Shreveport, Louisiana. Except for the pod damage, the DC-8 was structurally intact—another mute tribute to the jets' inherent strength. But 17 passengers were injured, 4 seriously enough to require hospitalization.

Not quite four months later, another Eastern DC-8—Flight 304—left New Orleans bound for Atlanta, Washington, and New York. Its wheels lifted at 2 A.M. Five minutes and forty seconds later, the giant plane crashed into Lake Pontchartrain, Louisiana, 19 miles northeast of the New Orleans International Airport. All 51 passengers and the 7 crew members perished. Among the latter was First Officer Grant Newby, who must have been living on borrowed time. The impact was so great that not a single whole body was recovered.

This was another turbulence accident but one in which turbulence was more a contributing factor than a primary cause. It revolved around a small device called the pitch trim compensator—PTC to pilots. The PTC is a means of offsetting a jet's tendency to "tuck under"—assume a nose-down attitude—at high speeds even while flying level. Mechanically, it consists of a tiny computer which senses the critical airspeed at which tuck-under occurs and automatically sends compensating electrical signals to an actuator. The actuator, in turn, moves the copilot's control column back, trimming the aircraft back to level attitude. The computer triggers the entire process either at Mach 70 (70 percent of the speed of sound) or at about 340 miles an hour. As speed increases, the computer steps up the electrical signals, which exert more force on the control yoke as the higher speed requires.

Boeing jets are not equipped with PTC units; pilot manipulation of the "pickle switch" accomplishes all trim chores. The DC-8 also has manual trim but the PTC was added to reduce the amount of trimming its crews would have to perform. Many DC-8 pilots would prefer to handle all necessary trim functions and would just as soon take the PTC off their planes. Others, however, regard it as a valuable aid.

The PTC on the Eastern jet that dove into Lake Pontchartrain was the subject of intensive investigation and, in fact, was the key to the crash. It is perhaps inconceivable to the layman that a malfunction in such a relatively tiny component—one that some pilots don't even regard as essential—could result in the destruction of a $6 million airliner. But to understand how it could happen is to understand better the phenomenon of jet behavior in turbulence, why the PTC was an undetected menace for so long, and the means by which this menace was overcome.

Above all, the case history of Eastern Flight 304 and the aircraft involved—N8607—confirms another aviation axiom: few accidents have a single cause. Rather, a crash invariably is the result of a combination of circumstances: a chain reaction of mistakes, omissions, and wrong assumptions, none fatal individually but deadly in a collective sense because each can lead to the fatal finality—whether it be pilot error, a failed part, or exposure to abnormal weather conditions. The fate of Flight 304 is a classic example.

The chain reaction that destroyed the EAL DC-8 began in that little PTC. The PTC computer on N8607 had been changed eight times, four in the week preceding the accident. And the computer that was on the jet when it crashed apparently deserved the automotive term "lemon." From April of 1960 to the night of the crash, this particular unit had been removed from various aircraft no less than fifteen times. Six of those removals followed pilot complaints of unwanted extension—in other words, the PTC actuated trim when it was not needed. Yet not a single discrepancy was found and the unit kept being reinstalled, the last installation being on N8607 the day before the crash. Not until after Flight 304 crashed was it learned why the PTC could malfunction in flight and yet pass every shop inspection. The reason was the initial triggering force that led to tragedy. *Not only Eastern but other DC-8 operators were performing PTC functional tests which were incapable of detecting certain computer malfunctions.*

This inspection inadequacy was discovered when CAB investigators took a supposedly serviceable unit from Eastern's PTC stock and put it through the manufacturer's own complete test procedures. The unit failed to pass all these more extensive tests.

On February 24, N8607 was flown from Miami to Philadelphia with no log complaints entered against the PTC. The aircraft was loaded for a flight to Mexico City via Washington, Atlanta, and New Orleans. Before leaving, the flight engineer reported that the PTC failed a ground check while he was going through his pre-takeoff checklist. Mechanics performed their own ground check and agreed with the flight engineer. That check consisted of activating the test circuit and watching for movement of the PTC indicator or control yoke. The mechanics did not inspect the actuator position or operating capability of the indicator system. The flight was dispatched with a request that the pilots check PTC operation during the trip south.

(It was ascertained later that no examination was made of the actuator because of its inaccessibility. To view the part, it was necessary to remove the copilot's seat. All DC-8s now have an access panel for easy actuator inspection, the panel being located in the nosewheel well.)

The crew performed the in-flight check between Washington and Atlanta and found the PTC inoperative. N8607 landed routinely at Mexico City the night of February 24 where its captain noted in the aircraft logbook that the PTC was inoperative and should be inspected and repaired when the ship returned to New York the next day.

Flight 304 departed Mexico City under command of Captain William Zeng, a veteran with more than 19,000 hours logged and nearly 1,000 of these representing DC-8 time. Because of the inoperative PTC, Zeng's flight plan—in accordance with Eastern's dispatch procedures—called for reduced airspeed all the way to New York. It turned out to be a futile precaution.

Passengers who disembarked at New Orleans said the Mexico City–New Orleans leg was routine except for light to moderate turbulence experienced in the last thirty minutes. There also was a cabin attendant change at New Orleans, a steward and three stewardesses replacing the four cabin attendants who had worked the Mexico City–New Orleans segment. First Officer Newby transmitted a "304 rolling" message to the tower fourteen seconds before 2 A.M. and the takeoff appeared to be normal.

One minute later, the New Orleans tower advised Flight

304 to contact Departure Control. Zeng, not Newby, acknowledged. The captain apparently had turned the controls over to the copilot immediately after takeoff. Personnel in the tower watched the anti-collision lights of the DC-8 disappear into an overcast about two and a half miles from the airport.

"Eastern 304, turn right heading zero-three-zero," Departure Control ordered.

The DC-8 banked obediently, as if giant puppet strings were attached to the wings.

At 2:02 A.M., Departure Control handed the flight over to the New Orleans Air Route Traffic Control Center and told Zeng: ". . . contact New Orleans Center, radar frequency one-two-three-point-six now."

"Okay," said Zeng.

This was the last word from Flight 304. About three minutes elapsed before the Center impatiently inquired of Departure Control:

"Did you send 304 over? He's not talking to me . . ."

"Yeah, I did," Departure Control assured the Center. "I'll shake him up again . . . Eastern 304, contact New Orleans Center, radar frequency one-two-three-point-six, now, please. Repeat. Eastern 304, contact New Orleans Center, radar frequency one-two-three-point-six . . ."

There was no answer. Departure Control, puzzled and now worried, asked the Center: "Hey . . . you got him?"

"No, I'm not talking to him . . . he disappeared off the scope . . . up there, northeast."

"Mine too," the controller manning Departure radar murmured.

"I don't know what happened," the Center said in a voice hollow with concern.

"Eastern 304 . . . one-two-three-four-three-two-one . . . Eastern 304 . . . New Orleans Departure Control calling."

No reply.

A controller in the New Orleans tower picked up a phone connected to Local Control.

"Give me a number for Eastern Air Lines," he snapped. Then, still on another line to the Center, he added: "Hey, Center, call the company, will you? We're trying to get a phone number now . . ."

Departure Control and the Center kept paging Flight 304. The former finally asked if state police should be notified. The Center agreed. Departure Control suggested that the police cars "run the Causeway over [Lake Pontchartrain] because he was in the vicinity of the Causeway on my scope . . . just east of it . . . yes he . . . he was."

Early the next morning, a helicopter spotted an oil slick and floating debris on the lake. The CAB immediately called in various kinds of electronic and sonic underwater detection gear, but the wreckage was not located until late in the afternoon of March 13. Salvage operations began immediately and continued on a twenty-four-hour basis until April 16. By that time, approximately 60 percent of the aircraft's torn carcass had been recovered from the mud and silt on the lake bottom. Each piece of wreckage was washed and then taken by barge to the New Orleans Lakefront Airport for examination by CAB, Douglas, Eastern, and ALPA experts.

There was no sign of structural failure, in-flight fire, or explosion. Examination of the engines disclosed that Zeng or Newby had taken the same desperate emergency action, apparently to halt a dive, which Captain French had employed to save another DC-8 from doom four months before. The recovered reverse assemblies showed use of reverse thrust at impact. The only trouble was that Flight 304's crew had run out of sky. They almost made it, at that; the power-plant damage indicated the jet was level at impact.

Both right and left stabilizer jackscrews were found within one turn of a full down position, which made no sense; the pilots obviously were trying to pull out of a dive and would not be applying nose-down trim. Then investigators discovered signs of abnormal wear in several parts that transmitted power to the stabilizer section, particularly failure of a chain sprocket on the stabilizer drive gear. To complete the picture of abnormal stabilizer functioning, the recovered portion of the PTC showed evidence of an "unprogramed" (meaning unwanted or inadvertent) extension. The PTC on N8607 was supposed to be inoperative. Yet it was evident that while the unit was inoperative, it actually had slipped into a nose-down trim condition. Far from being fully retracted, it was extended—sufficiently to give the pilots undesired down trim just as they ran into turbulence and a few other problems. To quote the CAB report issued sixteen months after the accident:

". . . the Board must accept the possibility that N8607, at departure from New Orleans . . . was being operated with a PTC actuator extension, although inoperative, ranging from 0.5 inch to 2.15 inches."

The CAB deduced that as Flight 304 climbed, the unwanted PTC extension literally jammed the stabilizers in down trim. With the aircraft accelerating in the climb, the pull forces on the controls must have increased steadily—to the point where it must have taken extreme exertion by the pilots to override the unprogramed down trim. At this point, it is reasonable to assume, Zeng and Newby reduced airspeed to relieve the unnaturally heavy stick (yoke) forces. This action presumably coincided with the encountering of moderate to severe turbulence. Suddenly the stick forces lessened with the reduction of airspeed, and simultaneously the DC-8 was shaken by turbulence gusts. Unprepared for the relieved stick forces, like a man on the end of a suddenly released rope, the crew overcontrolled the plane while trying to combat the oscillations, and Flight 304 went into a dive from which there was no room to recover.

That hypothetical picture of N8607's death throes is pure theory and, to some extent, second-guessing. But it is based not only on the inconclusive evidence of a malfunctioning PTC (the actuator itself was never located), but also on a number of subsequent test flights which drew an identical portrait.

As soon as the PTC became a prime suspect, Douglas conducted special test flights to determine DC-8 controllability with unprogramed PTC extensions or retractions. The company reported that even with this malfunction, adequate elevator control was available to overpower the unwanted PTC input.

Yet Douglas conceded there was a time lag for overriding what amounted to a stuck stabilizer—and there wasn't much time for Zeng and Newby at their relatively low altitude. Furthermore, later tests on DC-8s by FAA pilots revealed what the CAB termed "an interesting discovery." They showed that with a fully extended PTC, airspeed at approximately 220 knots (the estimated speed of Flight 304 when it went into its last dive) and the stabilizers trimmed fully down, any attempt to maneuver by using the elevator system resulted in extreme instability. To quote one FAA test pilot:

"This was true in applying either nose-up or nose-down control. A pilot with this condition existing during turbulent atmosphere would be presented with a very difficult control problem."

Another test pilot found that the combination of an unprogramed PTC extension and a down stabilizer setting seriously affected stick forces as airspeed varied—the forces shifting from very heavy to very light.

Still other test flights added more solidity to the CAB's theories about Flight 304. An independent research agency, under an FAA contract, conducted experiments involving the aerodynamic stability of swept-wing aircraft exposed to longitudinal motions—i.e., up and down turbulence. Said the CAB of these tests:

"Flight testing demonstrated . . . the aircraft could be flown with no difficulty as long as the pilot flew gently, accepting the slow response [of a jet being maneuvered through rough air]. If he attempted to force a more rapid response, as might be done in a gust disturbance, a short-period pilot-induced oscillation resulted. The pilots quickly found this characteristic could be overcome by smaller [lighter, easier or more gentle] corrections. However, it was disturbing to fly because one was never certain when a quick response might be needed."

The investigation of the New Orleans accident also turned up several cases of DC-8 control system misrigging among several airlines, a discovery which led to changes in maintenance procedures. Aside from this benefit, the misrigging cases provided additional evidence to buttress the CAB's reconstruction of what probably happened to N8607. In one instance, the crew on a DC-8 training flight reported control difficulties immediately after takeoff. An inspection disclosed that a new PTC actuator was extended a half inch even when it was fully retracted. The discrepancy resulted from an installation procedure that did not take into account a difference in the size of the bolts in the new unit, compared to those of an older model. On such apparent trivialities is potential disaster based. This misrigged PTC system, according to the pilots on the training flight, forced them to use nose-down trim following takeoff to such an extent that an excessive trim warning light flashed on.

In many respects, Eastern Flight 304 had as many beneficial aftereffects as Northwest 705 because it also shed new light on dark corners of unsuspected hazard. The circumstances differed, but the CAB's investigations delved into many mutual aspects—jet behavior in turbulence being a principal common denominator. While flight experts like Paul Soderlind of Northwest, Frank Kolk of American, and others in the industry preached new turbulence-handling techniques, parallel studies by the National Aeronautics and Space Agency fully supported their recommendations. I have dwelt on the turbulence problem at considerable length for a prime reason: it presented an air safety challenge associated almost exclusively with jets, and it was a challenge not fully appreciated at first—a failing which, if it cannot be alibied, can at least be explained and understood. It established one of the few patterns of danger in the first decade of the jets, and a pattern of trouble is easier to solve and correct than an isolated accident which has no apparent connection with other crashes.

Admittedly the pattern was deadly. The crash of a Trans-Canada (now Air Canada) DC-8 shortly after taking off from Montreal on November 29, 1963, was a mirror image of the crash of Flight 304. As late as August 1966, a Braniff BAC-111 disintegrated while trying to fly through a Nebraska thunderstorm. The British-built jet was the victim of an unusually powerful wind shear (a collision between the cold and warm air masses that spawn thunderstorms). The Braniff crash did not seem to fall into the loss of control in turbulence category, however. It was a case where the gust forces generated by the line squall simply exceeded the jet's stress limits, and this was not any example of jet vulnerability. Piston-engine planes have suffered structural failure in thunderstorms too; a wind shear can concentrate the equivalent destructive power of a tornado in a very small area. The weather encountered by the Braniff flight had been predicted and was avoidable; there was undoubtedly an element of overconfidence in airborne storm radar on the part of the captain, who thought he could pick his way through the storm. Overreliance on radar also was a factor in a subsequent Electra crash during a thunderstorm, and the National Transportation Safety Board has found it necessary to remind pilots that radar is intended as a storm-*avoidance* tool, not a device for flying through storms.

It is not being falsely optimistic to say that the upset menace has been drastically reduced, if not virtually eliminated. Altered cockpit techniques were only one of the reforms to come out of the deaths of two giant jets. The travel limit of horizontal stabilizers has been reduced in all jets to minimize the effects of mistrimming and prevent overtrimming. PTC inspections have been revised, Weather Bureau dissemination of thunderstorm warnings has been improved. Better instrumentation has been installed on the jet fleet, with new attitude displays giving pilots a true picture even in severely disturbed air.

These are the legacies left by Flights 705 and 304, and every passenger is a beneficiary. Still to be conquered is another kind of turbulence, however, one bearing the initials CAT.

They stand for Clear Air Turbulence. Never has CAT resulted in U.S. passenger fatalities, but it is a constant headache to pilots because it is so hard to predict and its onslaught is almost totally unexpected and frightening. It has caused minor structural damage and injuries. A form of low altitude CAT, frequently occurring just over mountain areas, was blamed for the fatal crash of a BOAC 707 on March 5, 1966, shortly after the jet had taken off from Tokyo International Airport bound for Hong Kong. BOAC pilots have a reputation for cautiousness, and what was to ensue was beyond explanation. The captain, Bernard Dobson, either decided to give his 114 passengers a breathtaking aerial view of Mount Fuji, the magnificent sacred cone that lies 55 miles from Tokyo, or it was his intention to expedite his departure from the Tokyo area by avoiding other IFR traffic on the normal climb route and conducting a visual climb via a Fuji shortcut.

The mountain is known to be a lair for violent winds. The weather itself was perfect—clear and sunny—but the forecasts predicted exceptionally strong winds in the Mount Fuji area at time of takeoff ranging from 85 miles an hour up to occasional gusts of 100 MPH, which is hurricane force.

Dobson, known as a prudent airman, checked the Tokyo weathermen before taking off, but it was never determined whether the particular forecasts he examined included high wind warnings for the Fuji area. It may be that he relied solely on visibility and ceiling information, which, of course, indicated perfect weather ahead. He also may have been guilty of overconfidence in his airplane—up to March

5, 1966, there probably was not a 707 pilot alive who thought a Boeing couldn't handle high winds.

Whatever the reasons behind his unfortunate decision, it was a fatal choice. Eyewitnesses saw the jetliner flying at upwards of 360 MPH toward huge spirals of snow that boiled up like white tornadoes over the mountain. The 707's altitude was almost level with Fuji's height, more than 12,000 feet. The aircraft seemed to fly between two of the visible twisters and it was as if two giant hands had grabbed the jet. Horrified onlookers on the ground saw the tail section separate from the fuselage, followed by the starboard wing. The 707 fell in flames. All 125 aboard were killed, including 90 Americans.

A Boeing official who aided the Japanese government in its investigation commented, after viewing the wreckage: "I never believed there could be destructive forces like this."

The BOAC 707 was wrecked by the winds and turbulence associated with high mountains, sometimes known as the mountain wave effect. This is not really CAT; it is more of a first cousin to the clear air turbulence which is prevalent at the higher altitudes. Airliners have been running into CAT for many years, but the jets are more frequently affected because they fly higher.

Research into CAT and means to avoid it dates back to before the advent of jets, but it has been stepped up considerably since 1960. CAT cannot be predicted by ordinary airborne radar, which measures turbulence only when it stems from precipitation. Thus, the radar on airliners is fine for warning pilots of storm turbulence—as far as 150 miles ahead. But CAT pounces without warning, out of what appears to be perfectly clear and smooth sky.

Technically, CAT is produced by a collision between two wind forces, one horizontal and the other vertical. The phenomenon is believed to be correlated with temperature changes at high altitudes. What the airlines have been seeking is an instrument capable of sensing these changes far enough in advance to permit avoidance. Back in 1960, an Eastern Air Lines weather expert named Paul Kadlec began riding jetliner jump seats as far north as Canada and as far south as Mexico, charting the conditions under which CAT is likely to occur.

Later, Eastern and also United equipped several jets with instruments registering the temperature of the air in their path. These early detection instruments registered temperature changes in fractions, on specially calibrated dials, but they still proved incapable of giving sufficient advance notice. Usually, the jets on which they were installed hit CAT just about the time the warning was being flashed.

But the temperature-sensing technique was promising enough to warrant refinement and further research. Scientists knew that turbulence, in effect, excites the molecules of the gases that make up the atmosphere. The molecules radiate increased energy which is measurable at several frequencies—such as an X-ray band or infrared waves. Excited gases, of course, rise in temperature, and this was the principle behind CAT detection methods.

In mid-1967, Pan American began flight-testing a CAT detection instrument that picks up the infrared frequency emitted by excited atmosphere. A few bugs have shown up, but the device has been undergoing constant modifications and refinements to the point where the airlines think CAT could be licked. Also encouraging is an Air Force-developed radar which has the theoretical capability of spotting CAT some distance ahead. The radar is so sensitive that it has tracked a single insect (a bee) twelve miles away.

There is widespread hope that CAT can be eliminated as a potential hazard—certainly in time for the supersonic age when no pilot would want to slam into turbulence at 1,800 miles an hour.

Despite this hope, however, CAT is far from a complete cure. The current research is typical of many air safety projects which hold so much potential that many in and out of aviation prematurely assume a particular problem has been licked and demand immediate implementation of unproved devices.

The system tested by Pan Am, for example, has some major failings in that infrared readings are not always accurate. A plane equipped with this type of sensor can get distorted readings when it flies into the sun. Reflections from clouds can produce false warnings. And while there is a definite connection between CAT and temperature changes, clear air turbulence also has been associated with such other atmospheric conditions as electrical fields. (12)

False turbulence warnings present a problem of their own. The early CAT sensors tested by the airlines and the

Air Force gave false turbulence indications 75 percent of the time, as well as providing insufficient warning when CAT was present. This seems to be a phenomenon of turbulence itself as well as an indication of the primitivity of the warning devices. Peter E. Kraght, manager of American Airlines' Weather Services, took a close look at the turbulence data collected by the airlines over a long period. He found that even when all the atmospheric conditions known to produce severe turbulence exist, pilots actually encounter rough air only 50 percent of the time. They run into light turbulence 40 percent of the time and experience moderate to severe turbulence only 10 percent of the time.

Nearly half of the world's fatal jetliner crashes in the past decade have occurred during the final approach or landing phase.

This is not any indication of jet vulnerability. The same statistic was true when piston-engine aircraft dominated commercial aviation. The statistic is more of an indication of failure to overcome known past hazards which have been allowed to continue into the jet age. The causes of approach/landing crashes apply to any airplane. That they still exist, in large part, is a partial exception to—almost a contradiction of—aviation's vaunted ability to learn from mistakes.

Inadequate airport facilities, unreliable altimeters, poor weather reporting—these three factors have been resulting in fatal accidents for the past thirty years and it is sad to admit that a major crash could occur tomorrow for one or a combination of those reasons. It is not that aviation has ignored them; the fact that airliners are operating safely and routinely in weather conditions responsible for grounding most flights only a few years ago is proof of progress. But the fact that the approach and/or landing phase of a flight remains the most dangerous is proof that not enough progress has been made.

Night landings, particularly those conducted in bad weather and/or over unlighted terrain or water, are beyond doubt the most dangerous.

A Boeing survey showed that between October, 1958, and December, 1967, there were 234 major commercial jet accidents and 82 of them occurred on approach and landing. Of the 82 landing crashes, 38 took place at night, over water or dark land, and toward lighted cities.

At one point early in 1969, the National Transportation Safety Board was investigating ten separate accidents, six of them occurring on approach to U.S. airports and five of these at night. Within a thirty-day period, Allegheny Airlines lost two Convair 540 prop-jets coming into the same airport—Bradford, Pa.—under identical weather conditions and again at night. Bradford happens to be among the two-thirds of the nation's airline-served airports which do not have as basic a landing aid as an Instrument Landing System. In other words, two out of every three U.S. airports provide airliners with an admittedly inadequate navigation and approach system. In effect, it guides planes only to the general area of an airport, unlike ILS which lines a flight up with the desired runway and tells a pilot if he is on the correct glideslope.

It is virtually unthinkable that in the eleventh year of the jet age, the majority of America's commercial airports lack such basically simple safety tools as ILS. Captain William Moss, whose safety survey was cited in an earlier chapter, has declared that the combination of night and lack of glideslope information in bad weather "is the single largest accident situation."

Politics and penny-pinching are largely responsible for a situation in which only 236 airports of nearly 600 served by the certificated carriers had ILS by early 1969. FAA doles out its limited funds ostensibly by need, but too frequently under the gun of political pressure. Bradford, for example, was supposed to get ILS more than a year before its two fatal crashes but the equipment went instead to a Florida airport—because of political intercession.

The FAA's appropriations for fiscal 1969 earmarked only $5.5 million for ILS installations at just 29 airports—including Bradford, in a classic case of locking the barn door after the horse is stolen. Five airports were granted funds to upgrade localizer beacons to full ILS systems. All this activity leaves about 300 airports still lacking ILS and if the Nixon administration continues its predecessor's spending pace, FAA will still be installing ILS ten years from now at airports which need the equipment right now. (13)

And the deficiency applies more than to just the airports served by the scheduled airlines. The air taxi business in the U.S. is booming to the point where in the near future it will need the same safety aids as the airlines themselves at airports the latter do not serve. All this was allowed to develop in face of obviously mushrooming air traffic in the midst of the jet age.

One refreshing and encouraging note came in 1969 from the comparatively small city of Latrobe, Pa., which commissioned the first non-federal ILS in the United States. The Westmoreland-Latrobe County Airport qualifies for both an FAA-installed control tower and ILS, but Airport Manager James Cavalier got tired of waiting for FAA funds. When FAA for the umpteenth time advised Cavalier it could not provide installation immediately, he ordered a $100,000 navaid and control tower package, including ILS, from Air Traffic Control Systems, Inc., Cleveland, Ohio.

"Safety demanded that we take the initiative and install the necessary navaids now," Cavalier explained. "While it is our hope that the government will someday take over the installation, we believe that the ATCS is so efficient and economical that we could simply not afford to delay. Our decision has already paid dividends in greatly improved safety and operational efficiency, and has significantly increased traffic."

If they ever give out medals to airport managers, Mr. Cavalier deserves to be standing near the front of the line. His action was a bright spot in a picture painted in the gloomy grays of delay and procrastination.

In 1962, the United States had a total of 219 ILS installations in operation at less than 200 airports. By 1969, seven years later, there were still less than 300 thanks mainly to the Federal Bureau of the Budget which not only kept slashing funds for ILS projects but reportedly warned FAA officials not to protest. Some of the lawsuits aimed at alleged airline negligence in landing accidents at inadequately equipped airports might better be directed at the real culprits.

ALPA has suggested that if the FAA can't get funds for badly needed ILS installations, it might use what money it does get more efficiently—for example, what the agency spends to buy and maintain a $46 million fleet of more than 100 planes. The union claims only a small portion of this fleet is necessary for such essential safety purposes as checking the accuracy of navigational systems. ALPA's estimate of minimum ILS requirements carries a $30 million price tag.

Most airports in the small or medium-sized category have only one ILS runway. If there is a system malfunction, no backup is available. A 1967 crash of a TWA Convair 880 at Cincinnati and the destruction of a Piedmont FH-227 at Charleston, W. Va., the following year had a common denominator: in both instances, the glideslope portion of ILS was inoperative.

The Air Force has developed relatively inexpensive temporary glideslope systems, although they are not adaptable to all airports because of terrain difficulties. And many small airports have just such terrain.

But the problem goes beyond the smaller airport. Crashes occur at major ones, too, where the jets need more sophisticated aids than ILS. One such aid is Precision Approach Radar (PAR), nothing but a fresher version of GCA (Ground Controlled Approach) which was used safely by thousands of military planes in World War II. Yet in the past year, the FAA has shut down no less than eight PAR installations at 14 large airports—partially because of a lack of skilled personnel to man them and partially because pilots refused to use them. Most airline pilots are inherently suspicious of any device that literally puts an aircraft into the hands of somebody on the ground.

(ALPA's unofficial position is that PAR can be dangerous in the hands of anyone but an exceptionally skilled controller and that there are too few such controllers available.) (14)

Provincial politics, too, has raised its ugly and cold-blooded head. Many airports are located so poorly as to constitute a perpetual safety menace. Charleston, W. Va., has one—built on top of a mountain with ever-present crosswinds. Pilots refer to it sarcastically as "the country's largest inland aircraft carrier." Officials would like to build a new airport at a better—and safer—location but the site selected would mean that the new field would be known as the Charleston/Huntington Airport. Sharing the "billing" honors with Huntington was such anathema to Charleston politicians that they succeeded in blocking the project, at least temporarily.

Chicago and Cleveland are among 25 cities considering new offshore airports, built on adjoining or nearby bodies of water. The concept has some merit, mainly in elimination of land-acquisition costs and reducing noise. But an offshore airport also may involve serious safety problems.

148

Weather visibility invariably is worse in the vicinity of water and most pilots hate approaches that take them over water, especially at night, when visual references are not only limited but often illusionary.

The latter is one of aviation's most underrated hazards. Boeing has a research project underway which already has produced some startling and disturbing results. Boeing engineers, concerned over the prevalence of accidents on approach and landing at night, built a "night visual approach simulator." In a two-week period, they put 12 experienced pilots through identical approaches to a make-believe city constructed on a tabletop in front of a cockpit simulator.

All 12 were told they were making a routine approach on a clear night to the "Nighterton Airport"—well-lighted and just south of the city, located on a three-degree slope. Bisecting Nighterton was a river. The city lights were bright but there were no lights between the approaching "aircraft" and the runway—a typical approach over water or unlighted terrain.

None of the pilots had altimeters for reference. They were told to concentrate on flying the best approach path possible, reporting their *estimated* altitude every 2 miles from 18 miles out. Their only usable instruments were an airspeed indicator and a vertical velocity indicator.

Of the dozen pilots, 11 crashed while making the approach. The closest any of the 11 got to the runway before "pranging" into the imaginary ground was 5 miles! One crashed a full 8 miles away.

They had been instructed to be at an estimated 5,000 feet while 10 miles out and at 1,240 feet 4.5 miles from touchdown. Except for a single pilot, all gave visual estimates of altitudes up to 2,500 feet higher than they really were. Yet these were Boeing jet instructors, men with thousands of hours of flight experience.

True, the dice was loaded against them. The supposedly safe airport was booby-trapped in a visual sense, accentuating every hazard inherent in such approaches from the lack of lights between the aircraft and runway to the slope of the terrain. The Boeing scientists in charge of the research emphasized, however, that to varying degrees these unsafe conditions are present at hundreds of airports. The scientists, Doctors Conrad Kraft and Charles El-worth, cited these typical and frequently occurring airport design errors: approach paths over darkness, either land or water; airports with unconventional widths and lengths; airports situated at a different altitude and on a different slope from the surrounding terrain; airports with a rise in their center sections; misleading light patterns from the adjoining cities and industrial smoke pollution which decreases the brightness of lights and makes them appear farther away.

Assuming that building new airports or drastically modernizing old ones may be financially impossible, the only solution is a means of guiding pilots to earth electronically and without the need for what now amounts to a totally visual operation beyond a certain altitude.

Is the task impossible?

Captain Robert Buck of Trans World Airlines is a pilot with great respect for government-industry air safety research. At the invitation of FAA Administrator Najeeb Halaby in 1963, Buck spent a month inspecting and studying the government's activities in solving bad weather operations. He was impressed with the dedication and talent of FAA personnel, but he was not impressed with the rate of progress. In his report to Halaby, he made this comment:

"In 1937, the landing limits for airliners at [airports like] Newark, New Jersey, were 200 feet ceiling and a half-mile visibility. These are the same limits today. We have jumped in speed during those 26 years from 170 miles per hour to 600, increased our range from 700 miles to more than 5,000, swelled passenger capacity from 14 to 140, but we have not gained one inch toward all-weather flying . . . we are about to land men on the moon, but we still cannot assure pilots and passengers of safely traversing the last two miles to an airport."

Buck's words were written five years ago, of course, and he would be the first to admit that steps of more than "one inch" have been taken toward all-weather operations since he made his report. But to some extent, his criticism remains valid. The U.S. airlines alone complete nearly 1 million instrument approaches a year, but the accident potential in bad-weather landings persists. Buck said at the time that his study convinced him there are no "unusual, different or badly neglected" weather problems but rather a general failure to use solutions already on hand. This, too, is still the case five years after his study. From the very start of the jet age, for example, pilots warned that too many runways were marginal in length for heavy jets trying to brake on slick surfaces. Overruns continue to plague the airlines, and while some are due to submarginal landing performances by pilots, many more can be blamed on submarginal runways.

Inadequate runways have played a major role in landing accidents, and there certainly is no mystery about either the problem or the solution. The FAA's original certification process theoretically required a jet to be able to stop in a certain distance on dry pavements, the distance depending on aircraft landing weight. The FAA itself admitted in 1965 that its requirements were on the unrealistic side—a concession that came in the form of an order increasing effective landing runway lengths by 15 percent under wet and/or icy conditions. For instance, a jet allowed to land on a 7,000-foot dry runway would need 8,500 feet of length if the runway were wet. If the longer runway was not available, the plane would have to reduce its landing weight—which in most cases means taking off passengers or cargo, or both. For the 15 percent increase in landing length minimums is predicted on runway conditions forecast as of a flight's estimated arrival time. Previously, runway length requirements were identical for dry and wet conditions.

(Overdue was the word for the FAA's action; forty-eight hours after the new rule was announced, to become effective January 15, 1966, a Continental Air Lines Boeing 707 landed on a rain-slick, 7,000-foot runway at Kansas City Municipal Airport—and kept rolling. The jet, with 59 passengers aboard, skidded past the end of the runway toward a dike. The captain managed to ground-loop and struck the dike sideways; a head-on collision probably would have been disastrous, but his action prevented any fatalities although the aircraft fuselage cracked open in two places.)

Pilots welcomed the stiffer regulation, even though they firmly believed a 40 percent increase would have been wiser. They still consider the FAA's additional safety margin inadequate at too many airports where the bigger jetliners literally squeeze their landings. A wet runway exposes any airplane to a hazard known as aquaplaning—and one captain said of this condition, "When aquaplaning starts, the pilots might as well be back in the cabin with the passengers."

Aquaplaning to an airman is simply the loss of tire friction on a wet surface, and it can be as scary as an automobile skidding on glare ice. In fact, automobile drivers encounter aquaplaning of a sort. It occurs most frequently in the early stages of a rain that hits a dry pavement. The combination of water on a surface containing residues of oil, before the rain has a chance to wash away the oil, drastically reduces braking force.

In the case of a heavy aircraft, a film of water on a runway can have the same effect. The plane keeps rolling, resisting all efforts to brake because the tire tread never really touches the pavement. Compounding the aquaplaning problem, surprising to relate, is noise abatement! It seems that some noise abatement procedures result in pilots landing downwind instead of upwind, which increases both the landing speed and the chances of aquaplaning. A Pan Am jet landing downwind at Kennedy International Airport a few years ago aquaplaned off the runway. All 145 persons aboard walked away from the wreckage, and if they could have known the facts they would have been 145 persons who never again complained about noise annoyance.

Runway length is one of those areas in which pilots could be forgiven for muttering "I told you so." The Air Line Pilots Association since 1948 has been urging the federal government to certificate airports for safety just as it certificates aircraft. It makes no sense, according to pilots, to assure the public it is riding on safe airplanes that have to land at unsafe airports. The official ALPA policy on the subject demanded not only adequate runways but also adherence to minimum standards in all aspects of airport operations, from snow removal to elimination of obstructions on approach paths.

From the standpoint of an airline pilot, or that of a passenger, the ALPA policy does not seem unreasonable. There is evidence that the FAA agrees. In June of 1967, the agency began making experimental safety inspections of 32 major airports "to identify conditions within the airport environment which may contribute to accidents or incidents, inform airport managers of unsafe or marginal conditions, evaluate the willingness and effectiveness of managers in taking corrective actions recommended as the result of the inspections, and estimate the FAA resources required to perform the safety inspections if the agency decides they are needed."

According to *Aviation Daily,* the first 12 airports checked turned up "improperly or poorly maintained runway marking, improper or non-uniform runway and taxiway light spacing or orientation, poorly maintained or eroded runway shoulders or lips, poor public protection and airport fencing, marginally manned or marginally equipped fire rescue facilities, inadequate safety precautions in fueling areas and improper locations for wind recording devices."

ALPA believes the FAA should be armed with authority to certificate airports as it does pilots and aircraft, which admittedly would put some teeth into the inspection process. FAA itself prefers continuing inspection rather than regulation by certification, on the grounds that the latter by law requires formal hearings in order to withdraw a certificate.

"To get some holes in a runway filled, you'd have to hold a hearing that could last a couple of months," one FAA official comments.

The FAA also has been asked to certificate airport managers—again supported by ALPA—which the managers themselves strongly oppose. The American Association of Airport Executives, which actually has its own accrediting program for airport management, points out that certification based solely on safety ignores the equally important tasks of administration and financing. The managers themselves are divided on the necessity for certification. They are conscientious, hard-working men who are not unaware of safety problems and their own inadequacies, but who point out that the inadequacies usually are the result of lack of money, not indifference. In this respect, Congress is a prime offender; it has persistently slashed appropriations for federal aid to airports, the economy advocates usually including those more vocal members fond of denouncing the airline industry and FAA for not doing more to improve safety.

The airlines, until recently, were not without some guilt in the field of inadequate airports. For a long time, airport officials have complained bitterly that they have never been able to obtain facts or figures or even a majority

153

agreement from the carriers on what airport improvements might be needed in the future.

"If the airlines would tell the airports what their realistic requirements will be five to ten years hence," Foster Jones, director of airports for Louisville, Kentucky, told the 1967 ALPA safety forum, "and sit down with us with the idea of working together for their development to the benefit of the community and the airline, we would have far better airports today. This head-in-sand attitude has been one of the greatest detriments to the development of airports."

Fortunately, the airlines appear to be taking their heads out of the sand, as Jones put it. United Air Lines for two years has had a special staff analyzing every airport it serves with a view to determining what is needed in terms of airspace utilization, runway capabilities, airport access, and terminal facilities for passengers and cargo. And the Air Transport Association in 1967 set up an industry-wide committee to work with airport management on correcting present weaknesses and planning for future needs.

Much of this new spirit of airline-airport cooperation, of course, deals with service as well as safety. In the latter respect, airport operators readily concede room for improvement, but they express some natural cynicism toward FAA's growing "shape up or else" mood. Jones, in his ALPA speech, was just one of many airport managers who think the federal government—in almost inevitable bureaucratic inconsistency—figuratively shakes one fist self-righteously while committing sins of its own with the other. Said Jones wryly, as he recited one example:

"The FAA has a requirement for the painting of automobiles used on airports to the effect that they should be high-visibility yellow. This is an excellent idea because they can be seen from the tower and the air, and it also gives the tower operator immediate identification of a stranger who doesn't belong there. Who is the biggest violator? The FAA and the Air Force, promulgators of the regulation! The FAA uses those gray GSA (General Services Administration) vehicles and the Air Force has blue vehicles, two of the hardest colors to see on an airport."

The Louisville airport official also recounted an incident involving a needed runway extension. In order to get federal funding assistance, it had to be built in accordance with guidelines laid down by the FAA's Airport Design

Manual. That manual permitted open drainage ditches along or across the ends of runways and within 175 feet of the edge.

Jones went out one day to check the runway construction and found the contractor installing a retaining wall in a ditch 10 feet deep— "He was doing," Jones added, "just what the FAA said . . . needless to say, the ditch isn't there now, but it sure took a lot of argument, phone calls and proof which I had to obtain in the form of statements from ALPA, ATA and others to get a drainage pipe put in."

This may seem like a picayunish gibe at an agency which for the most part does a superb job for aviation. But it is presented along with a gentle reminder that little things cause big accidents—like a one-inch bolt, or a half-inch unwanted extension in a tiny motor, or a ten-foot ditch at the end of a runway on which a jet may not be able to stop in time.

There is, however, a tendency to pick on the airports as scapegoats for the airport safety problem, a problem which can be defined simply as a case where aviation technology has outstripped the airport itself. But a more objective examination uncovers other culprits, such as, to repeat, Congress. Says one prominent airport official:

"Airports have been running to catch up with airplanes since 1945, largely because federal aid has been so erratic that long-range planning has been impossible."

The Airport Operators Council estimates that federal aid to the tune of about $160 million a year is needed to modernize the nation's airports between now and 1970. Naturally, part of this amount would go for services rather than safety, but by no means the majority. A sizable proportion would have an indirect bearing on safety —such as money to build new general aviation airports that would relieve the major terminals of light plane traffic. Yet current Congressional appropriations call for spending only $71 million annually, less than half of what the airports and airlines say is needed.

The Department of Transportation is trying to unplug a little-appreciated bottleneck in airport improvement by emphasizing the interdependency of all facets of air transportation. There has been too little planning on a national scale, due largely to the failure of a provincially minded Congress to understand the complexity of a modern transportation system. It does little good to have a huge terminal and inadequate runways or, conversely, a tiny terminal and huge runways. It is a waste of time to have a modern airport served by totally inefficient ground transportation. Yet when Congress enacted the Federal Aid to Airports Act, typically it saddled the law with countless restrictions which, in effect, ignored interdependency.

Certainly, there was pitifully little advance planning done for the jet age as far as airports were concerned—not at the major cities, but in the smaller ones which clamor for jet service into airports where the jets would need figurative shoehorns. The Association of Local Transport Airlines, representing all but one of the nation's local service airlines, has a membership operating in and out of more than 500 airports. As of mid-1969, they were operating under various weight restrictions at 378 of these airports.

The phrase "weight restrictions" is synonymous with inadequate runways, and even when runways are improved there is a temptation on the part of many financially hard-pressed airports to bring them up merely to minimum requirements instead of building in extra safety margins.

Not even the bigger airports are exempt from sinning against safety. They are not dangerous per se—not when millions of landings are made safely every year—but their ability to provide safety under *all* conditions varies to a considerable degree. It might be said that too many of them are only marginally safe under certain conditions. Captain Homer Mouden of Braniff, a leading ALPA expert on landing problems, made this comment in observing that marginal runways can cause difficulties ranging from annoyance to catastrophe: "The margin between the two extremes is often as narrow as the thickness of an aircraft's skin."

Continued Mouden: "Overruns are caused initially by one or a number of unavoidable [and usually compounded] conditions—slippery runways, worn or smooth tires, crosswinds, and high or fast approaches due to adverse weather—but the causal factor of all overrun accidents or incidents is that runways are too short for operating under those conditions encountered at that time . . . They have remained the same causative factors for more than twenty years, with no significant change in them during the past ten years of jet airline operation."

There are two primary ways to slow down and stop a

jetliner when the wheels are on the ground—reverse thrust and brakes. Both are extremely efficient considering that they have to dissipate the energy generated by 120 tons of metal moving at 90 to 130 miles an hour. Aircraft brakes are far better, proportionately, than automobile brakes. The capability of this system has more than doubled in efficiency since 1950, improving so much that some pilots believe this probably has resulted in lethargic research into finding other means of stopping airplanes.

But the finest braking and reverse thrust systems in the world can be useless during aquaplaning. And there are circumstances in which pilots cannot use full braking or full reverse thrust—during severe crosswinds, for example. Under these conditions, adequate runway length must substitute for braking efficiency. And under truly abnormal conditions, such as unavoidable aquaplaning, even a long runway can be insufficient. This is why pilots also urge that runways have strong overrun areas, capable of withstanding a jet's weight and providing just an extra margin of safety that could mean the difference between a harmless overrun of the runway itself or a disastrous collision with soft turf and/or obstacles at the end of a runway.

A layman might ask why it is necessary for a skilled pilot to need so much protection—evidently, it might be said, against his own occasionally faulty technique. With rare exceptions, it is not faulty technique that gets a pilot into trouble during a landing. U.S. airline pilots have made about 50 million safe jet landings since 1958. In 1960, NASA did a survey of landing patterns and practices which revealed that the overwhelming majority of pilots landed in just about the same way—in almost every case they used up the same amount of runway before touching down, for example. Two years later, the FAA did a similar survey, which showed that most pilots still weren't deviating in the ways they were landing. as the survey emphasized, they were adhering to the "fly 'em by the book" rule hammered into all jetliner crews. There was a bothersome tendency noted in both surveys, however,—namely a propensity to "duck under" the glide path slightly during the final visual portion of approach and landing. This could be conducive to undershooting, which is potentially a worse hazard than overshooting. Yet the latter occurs far more frequently and it is obvious that the duck-under habit is not what is causing most runway accidents and incidents.

The frequency of these mishaps can be judged by the experience of just one major airline, which happens to have one of the best safety records in the world and a pilot training program that is copied by other carriers. This airline has averaged, during the jet age, about 2 undershoots for every 1 million landings, 4 overshoots per 1 million landings, and a slightly higher occurrence of runoffs for every 1 million landings. Each instance represents a potential accident even if one did not occur. The record for the entire industry shows more than $33.2 million worth of jets destroyed in overrun mishaps since 1958.

It should not be supposed that nobody is doing anything about all this. If more-than-adequate runways are the answer, and it undoubtedly is, what can be accomplished until better runways are built? One solution is not only promising but far beyond the experimental stage. This is the grooved runway, or, as pilots and airport officials have dubbed it, the "runway stretcher."

The nickname is well deserved. Runway grooving involves placing strips of tiny indentations across the width of a runway to reduce or even eliminate aquaplaning and skidding. One of the first test grooving installations was at the much-criticized Kansas City Municipal Airport after preliminary tests on a NASA runway at Wallops Island, Virginia. The Kansas City grooves, only an eighth of an inch wide, a quarter of an inch deep, and less than two inches apart, covered 4,500 feet of a 7,000-foot runway. The immediate results: skid resistance improved about 20 percent under both wet and dry conditions. The airport manager reported to the Air Transport Association, which originated the project, that since grooving the one runway there had been almost no diversions to the neighboring Kansas City International Airport (where runways are longer) during heavy rains.

Runways also have been grooved at Washington National, Chicago's Midway, Charleston, W. Va., and Kennedy International. In most cases the airlines shared the cost by agreeing to increased landing fees (an airline pays, incidentally, $75 to land a four-engine jet at JFK; $34 at Los Angeles; $331 in Paris; $522 at Prestwick, Scotland; and a whopping $1,007 at Sydney—an operating cost of which most passengers are unaware). Installation at Kansas City ran $87,000 and $178,000 at JFK. Atlanta at this writing was grooving one runway and Boston was planning to groove a runway at Logan International. Meanwhile, FAA and NASA are testing a means of casting concrete with grooves for airports building a brand-new runway; the casting technique would be considerably cheaper.

At both Washington and Kansas City, grooving proved to be so effective that pilots reported their anti-skid devices weren't even being activated on wet days. Walter Horne, NASA's expert on runway traction, told ATA that all the test data indicated grooving literally turned a wet runway into a dry one. And the majority of airline pilots questioned on their reactions to grooved pavements urged the grooving of all runways equipped with instrument landing systems—in other words, those most frequently used during bad weather.

Grooving is relatively inexpensive safety insurance, compared to the cost of lengthening a runway or installing such devices as arresting gears. A rough ball-park figure is that it would run between $70,000 and $100,000 to groove the full length and width of a runway 10,000 feet long and 150 feet wide. Whether the airports, airlines, federal government, or a combination of the three should pay the bill is a matter to be settled. What is more important is that grooving seems to work, it is not exorbitantly expensive and it can be done quickly. The British (who often are ahead of everyone when it comes to solving some air safety problems) have been grooving runways at military airports for more than twelve years. Both the British and NASA techniques utilized high-speed diamond cutting wheels which carve out thirteen grooves at a time. The job at the JFK runway was started May 8, 1967, and finished the following July 24—which is a lot faster than what it would have taken to stretch the same runway by 2,000 feet (at a cost of $1000 per linear foot!).

Pilots have been unable to tell the difference between a grooved runway and conventional ones. The first U.S. captain to experience grooving was an American Airlines pilot taking delivery in England on a new BAC-111. ATA officials asked him to land the jet on a grooved British runway, half-expecting him to report that it felt like going over a washboard road in an automobile—as some aviation authorities in this country feared. His verdict:

"I couldn't spot any difference from what I was used to. There was no vibration, noise or rumble of any kind."

One possible objection to grooved runways is the possibility that they could accumulate water and eventually overflow into one huge puddle. It isn't likely, given anything short of a prolonged cloudburst capable of drowning the Ark itself. The 8,400-foot grooved runway at JFK has 104 million inches of grooves which hold 11,000 gallons of water, or 93,000 pounds.

The runway at Kennedy, it should be noted, is used only for landings. ATA and FAA are gathering further data on whether a grooved runway would have any effect on take-off performance. It may be that grooving will be limited to landing runways exclusively, although right now there is very little evidence indicating adverse effects on takeoffs.

Significantly, airline pilots continue to call for better runways and express enthusiasm over grooving as being at least a step in the right direction, but they have demonstrated very little support for runway arresting gears, which some lawmakers have pressured the FAA to make mandatory at all major airports.

Runway arresting gears are a direct descendant of a similar device used since the twenties on aircraft carriers, to bring Navy planes to a quick stop when landing on carrier decks. The gear works, too. I was aboard an FAA Boeing 720 on a gear test a few years ago. The 100-ton jet engaged the gear at a speed of well over 100 miles an hour and came to a swift, not uncomfortable stop in about five seconds—only a few feet from the end of the runway.

The device is relatively simple. Steel cables are wound around huge drums embedded on each side of a runway. A small section of cable stretches across the runway, just high enough to catch a retractable hook attached to an aircraft's belly. The hook is lowered to cable height by the pilot's pushing a button, when he realizes that an overrun is inevitable. The jet's weight and momentum unwinds the cable from its lubricated drums.

In commercial use, the gear would be located about 2,000 feet from either end of the runway. Installation for a single runway costs about $250,000–$300,000, but an added expense is the necessity of stressing aircraft frames to accommodate the hook structure and withstand the strain of engagement. This would run about $5,000 per plane on jets already built, although less if the hook arrangement were built into a brand-new airframe at the factory. Some Boeing 727s already have been turned out with special modifications for the hooks.

A somewhat similar but less complicated device is a self-erecting net made of lightweight but immensely strong synthetic fibers. One has been demonstrated in France and it has the advantage of eliminating the heavy, cumbersome steel cables that are part of runway arresting gears. The French net barrier was designed specifically to serve as a safety measure during tests of the Concorde, the British-French supersonic transport.

The net is stored in a trench dug across the runway end. It can be activated by a signal either from an airplane or the control tower. The webbing has just enough elasticity to slow a heavy jet, with the dynamic loads being shifted from the net to a friction-braking assembly located on either side of the runway.

Designers claim impact damage to whatever aircraft struck the net would be minimal—certainly less than what would occur during an overrun. In theory, anyway, it appears to be more practical than the cumbersome arresting gear which requires considerable time for rewinding the tons of cable and restoring the gear for use—a process sufficiently complicated to force the closing of the runway over a two- to four-hour period.

The net or gear concept could have saved lives in the past. One example was the crash of an Air France 707 at Orly Field, Paris, in June, 1962. The jet failed to get airborne on takeoff, overran the runway, and burst into flames. One hundred and thirty persons died, including many prominent residents of Atlanta, Georgia.

Gear proponents point out that the device has been used at many military fields, saving hundreds of lives. This is true, but the Air Force and Navy use arresting gears largely for fighters with high landing speeds. They have never installed hooks on their large bombers or transports, relying instead on long runways and adequate overrun areas—something, again, which airline pilots prefer to arresting devices.

The FAA, airlines, and most safety experts agree, feeling that the funds necessary for gear or net installations would be better spent in such areas as overrun and undershoot "buffer" zones, longer runways, grooved runways, and post-impact fire suppression systems. (15)

A possible compromise might be the installation of arresting devices on the shorter runways which, for reasons of cost or geography, cannot be lengthened or protected by overrun real estate. Runway length can be misleading, as a matter of fact, because the full length is not always available to pilots. A runway at Boston's Logan International Airport, for example (one which has had several overrun accidents) is 10,000 feet long—ostensibly more than adequate. But the glide path used by pilots flying instrument approaches to this runway takes them to a touchdown point more than 3,400 feet from the threshold —leaving them just under 6,600 feet for the roll-out.

Another means of lengthening runways without adding a foot of additional real estate is boundary layer control. Boundary layer is simply the region of retarded air that builds up near the surface of a body moving through the air. The original Boeing 707 prototype, old "Dash-80," was fitted with boundary layer control devices a couple of years ago—literally a system for increasing the airflow under the wings during the approach and landing phase. Touchdown speed for a 707 or DC-8 will range between 117 and 138 knots depending on gross weight and temperature. Dash-80, equipped with boundary layer control, was landed consistently at just over 80 knots and the stall speed was reduced to that of a small aircraft—below 60 knots. Approach speeds were reduced from around 145 knots to 85 knots, which gave the Dash-80 the capability of landing under gross load conditions on a 4,000-foot runway.

Obviously boundary layer control could be a means of virtually eliminating undershoots, overshoots, aquaplaning, and myriad other menaces to safe landings. Unfortunately it is an enormously expensive installation. To equip present jets with a proven, effective boundary layer control system would run about $1 million per aircraft and probably as much as half that amount on a new jetliner. Airlines and manufacturers alike must weigh that $1 million price tag against the cost of the accidents boundary layer control would prevent, and it may well be that the cure is too costly for the seriousness of the disease. There seems to be far less interest in putting BLC systems in the new jumbo jets, largely because the limited major airports they will serve have more than adequate runways.

Runway length, of course, is a vital factor in another

type of airport crash—the takeoff accident. This category has accounted for about 5 percent of fatalities in the jet age's first decade. While occurrence is far less frequent than that of landing and approach crashes, the results can be just as bad and the cures just as obvious. If a runway is too short for any out-of-the-ordinary landing, to a somewhat lesser extent it may be too short for a takeoff that goes sour.

The critical V_1 speed condition already has been explained in this book. If any engine fails during the takeoff roll, a pilot must stop before he reaches V_1. Beyond V_1 there is no choice: the pilot must continue his takeoff and get airborne on his remaining engine or engines. The V_1 of every jet is computed carefully before every takeoff, because it varies with aircraft weight, outside temperatures, the height of the airport above sea level, and the length of the runway.

One classic example of a takeoff accident was the crash of a TWA 707 at Cincinnati on November 6, 1967. The jet began to roll with its crew unaware that a Delta DC-9 was stuck in the mud, off to one side of their assigned runway. The jet was still short of V_1 when the pilots spotted the mired Delta plane. It appeared uncomfortably close. As the TWA jet screamed by, its pilots were startled by a loud noise, a kind of boom. Their immediate reaction was that they had collided with Delta—the TWA copilot, who was at the controls, shouted, "Good God, I hit him!"

Actually, there had been no collision. The loud boom had come from an extremely infrequent type of engine backfire at the precise moment the 707 was passing the DC-9. But thinking a collision had occurred, the TWA crew instantly aborted the takeoff, applying brakes and going into full reverse thrust.

The runway was 7,800 feet long. Their V_1 speed was 132 knots. At the moment they decided to abort, they were doing 143 knots—11 above abort speed and only 7 knots below V_2 or liftoff speed. The odds were against a successful abort and the jet failed to stop at runway edge, plowing into a field and catching fire. Thanks to swift and efficient emergency procedures all aboard got out safely, but this was an accident illustrating the thin margin of safety existing in runways that are completely safe only in normal circumstances.

There also can be somewhat of a margin between the

conditions of a certification test and an actual emergency. Dave Hoffman of the Washington *Post,* in a well-written analysis of the Cincinnati crash, succinctly explained the difference between certification tests and actual emergencies, emphasizing that the average pilot has only four seconds to recognize the nature of the emergency, decide what action to take, and then take that action. In four seconds, a jet will have eaten up another thousand feet of runway and continued to accelerate another 20 knots—in which time V_1 may well have been exceeded. Added Hoffman:

"To determine the 707's runway length requirements, Boeing used a team of crack test pilots. It gave them a brand-new 707 with brand-new brakes. The 707's tires, fresh from the factory, were perfectly round and had deep, finely grooved treads. Installed on the 707's instrument panel was an oversized airspeed indicator that registered velocity in fractions of knots.

"Instead of staging the tests on a runway slickened by engine oil and jet exhaust particles, the pilots used a long stretch of dry, clean concrete. But more important, the men knew what lay in store as they sped down the runway."

In 1963, the FAA proposed a new regulation which in effect added 800 feet to V_1 runway margins; i.e., if a jet grossing a certain weight was supposed to be able to stop, say, in not more than 7,000 feet, the new allowable stopping distance would be only 6,200 feet. The airlines and manufacturers protested, the former on the grounds that the rule would impose heavy economic penalties and the latter with the argument that test data plus certification standards were more conclusive safety evidence than fears expressed by a handful of airline pilots.

Increasing the so-called "accelerate-stop distance" could only have been accomplished by reducing jet pay loads at a number of cities. The airlines asserted that millions of safe takeoffs and scores of successful aborts negated the danger signals raised by some pilots on the basis of infinitesimally few unsuccessful aborts. The FAA scrapped its proposed regulation. There is room for debate on its wisdom, but here again is a situation where a stiffer rule would be unnecessary if runways were adequate.

The fact that the airlines objected to a rule which admittedly would have provided an extra safety margin may prompt the layman to believe the oft repeated criticism that the industry invariably puts economics ahead of safety. This is hogwash. Without safety, airline profits would nosedive faster than a stalled jet. It is true that on occasions the airlines have made woefully wrong decisions involving economics-vs-safety. As an industry, the airlines originally fought mandatory installation of weather-warning radar, and fortunately they lost the fight. A handful of carriers, led by United, supported such a regulation, and UAL, in fact, equipped its entire fleet with radar long before the FAA got around to making it mandatory. It is to the industry's credit that every airline later admitted that United and FAA were right.

Nor is the industry's balking on some safety proposals a legitimate indication that profits are being put ahead of safety. The airlines have a very logical right to ask whether a safety recommendation actually enhances safety to a degree that warrants huge expenditures. For every indefensible airline objection, such as rejection of storm-warning radar, one could find a half-dozen objections which were justified because they were raised against safety ideas that were not thoroughly tested, that were premature or that created new problems even as they solved an old one.

One also could find a myriad of instances where safety advances have been generated to a great extent by the airlines themselves. Nowhere is this more true recently than in the area of "the last two miles" and the prevention of bad-weather accidents. In the past three years, there have been incredible strides toward fulfillment of aviation's fondest dream—the ability to operate safely and without undue delay under zero visibility and ceiling conditions, or the kind of weather "in which even the birds are walking." Much of the research, testing, and funding has come from the FAA, but what progress has been made never would have gotten off the ground without airline enthusiasm, support, and technical cooperation.

There are obvious economic benefits to be derived from making the last two miles a lot safer. In this case, however, economic and safety benefits are synonymous.

A prime example of airline-fostered safety action is the battle against one of the airman's oldest enemies—fog.

The first attempt to dissipate fog artificially occurred during World War II when the Air Force burned high-octane gasoline at English air bases so bombers could land after missions. The technique was successful and further experiments were conducted in California after the war, but the gas-burning method proved too expensive to be practical.

On December 26, 1963, a small plane flew over the fog-choked Salt Lake City airport and dropped pellets made of dry ice.

The plane had been chartered by United Air Lines, which had a jetliner grounded by the fog. UAL officials were waiting for just such a moment to test a fog-seeding technique in which they had become intensely interested. As soon as the Salt Lake City airport was closed to all airline traffic, they called Intermountain Weather, Inc., a local cloud-seeding company that UAL had retained for the winter.

Intermountain put 80 pounds of crushed dry ice into a Beech Bonanza and circled the airport. The ice was dropped through a temporary slit in the plane's belly, using an ordinary fertilizer spreader. In less than ten minutes, the fog began to lift and visibility increased to a half mile, allowing the United jet to take off. The pellets continued their dispersal effect for nearly four hours.

The next night, fog again closed down the airport and United ordered another seeding "raid." Twenty minutes later, the fog had lifted enough to reopen the field and permit takeoffs by five flights. The experiment was tried a third time on December 30 when a United jet flying in from the East Coast was unable to land because of heavy fog. Once more the pellets were dropped and the jet landed safely.

United spread the word throughout the industry. The three "raids" saved this one airline thousands of dollars by preventing cancellations or delays that would have affected 226 passengers on 7 airplanes, not to mention the safety aspects.

UAL was understandably cautious in its optimism. The type of fog prevalent in the Pacific Northwest is known as the "supercooled" variety—it occurs in below-freezing weather. The dry ice seeding works only with this kind of fog. When the pellets contact the fog, a chemical reaction takes place which causes water particles to change to ice crystals. This results in an extremely fine snow that releases moisture and dissipates the fog.

In the winter of 1964, United "bombed" seven more Pacific Northwest cities afflicted with supercooled fog—

Seattle/Tacoma, Portland, Spokane, Reno, Pendleton, Medford, and Boise. The technique was used on fourteen separate occasions. The accumulative results: the pellets evaporated fog sufficiently to allow takeoffs or landings by thirty flights carrying more than 700 passengers.

To the communities involved, United had given this argument in support of its contention that fog dispersal is an airport responsibility, the same as runway maintenance and snow removal. Said United, in effect:

"Try the experiment at your own airports. Fog seeding costs money [$65 per flight in the original Salt Lake City experiments]. But you'll get it back and maybe more through landing fees. If planes can't land, you don't collect anyway. At airports like Medford and Pendleton, where landing fees are based on scheduled landings, United and other airlines will underwrite the cost."

United picked these airports, plus Salt Lake City, on the basis of an unpublicized five-year study by UAL meteorology experts. They found that supercooled fog prevailed an average of 208 hours at Medford, 149 at Spokane, 108 at Pendleton, 96 at Boise, 65 at Salt Lake City, 46 at Reno, 31 at Portland, and 25 at Seattle/Tacoma.

United wanted a concerted government-industry effort to continue the tests on a wider scale. The FAA, concentrating funds and talent on electronic all-weather landing systems, didn't show much interest. Other airlines, while impressed, pointed out that seeding supercooled fog would be of benefit mainly at airports on UAL's Pacific Northwest routes and would be of little use at cities on their own systems. How about warm-air fog, they asked—which is the culprit at 95 percent of the nation's airports?

Late in 1967, the Air Transport Association plunked down $100,000 for a new series of tests, these to be aimed at the more prevalent warm-air fog. The city picked for the experiments was Sacramento, California, where this type of fog persists throughout the winter months. On the average, fog shuts down the Sacramento airport more than 40 hours during December alone.

The ATA project utilized a variety of new chemicals for the seeding. In charge was W. Boynton Beckwith, chief meteorologist of United, assisted by weather specialists from several other carriers. It would have been more spectacular if the defogging technique was tried at a huge airport like O'Hare or Kennedy, but this was impractical because of their heavy traffic. Besides, Sacramento is peculiarly susceptible to fog conditions which even resist the usual dissipation under morning sunlight—"a very persistent type," Beckwith explained.

The ATA tests ran from November 15, 1967, to March 8, 1968. In that period, the Sacramento Municipal and Metropolitan Airports were shut down by fog on 46 days. A total of 36 seeding flights were made on 26 days, but only 27 of these flights were evaluated in terms of whether they achieved the standard of a successful seeding—namely, opening up an airport that had been closed because of fog. The other nine were practice or "warm-up" missions.

Of the 27 flights, 19 were successful or partially successful—or 70 percent of the total. There were 4 failures and 4 flights judged to be inconclusive. The 4 "flunked" operations included one flight in which the chemicals had been diluted, one in which the control tower couldn't see the runway although pilots reported it had been cleared, one in which wind carried the chemicals away from the runway and opened up a hole over the city itself, and one in which the seeding aircraft had to abandon the test because the tower had conflicting traffic.

ATA said a study of climatological data showed that the 19 successful flights resulted in opening the airport two to four hours earlier than would have been possible through natural fog dissipation.

By early 1969, there were additional warm and cold fog dispersal tests being conducted at 17 airports, the airlines generally sharing the costs through temporarily increased landing fees. The carriers hope to earn happy dividends on their investment for fog is a financial as well as safety burden.(16)

Delays and cancellations due to fog cost the airlines an estimated $144 million annually; fog is responsible for most of the 61,000 flight cancellations that occur in an average year. ATA believes a nationwide artificial fog dispersal program would cost about one fifth that amount—and the financial penalty of fog does not include the cost of aircraft which have been wrecked in fog accidents. There will be no nationwide adoption of seeding warm fog, however, until the technique has been fully perfected. The Navy found out the hazards of premature assumptions when it dropped ammonium nitrate into thick clouds in a related cloud dissipation experiment.

The chemical burned holes through a low cloud layer 3,000 feet thick, enabling aircraft to descend through the holes and land. This was according to plan. What was not planned was the effect of ammonium nitrate on aluminum! For the chemicals also burned holes through aircraft skin and all the test planes had to be repaired with fresh skin patches.

"Bombarding" fog from the air, of course, has its own weather hazards. The ATA-financed tests are largely to evaluate the effectiveness of various chemicals; more practical fog dispersal methods probably will involve application on the ground instead of from the air. One device to be tested is a series of long tubes containing compressed air, and located alongside the runway. With the touch of a button, the tubes could blast chemicals into the air above the runway. ATA has been testing a modified orchard sprayer equipped with a 100-foot tube that propels dispersing chemicals another 100 feet into the air. Technicians have dubbed it "the jolly green giant."

Government-funded research has been trying out a means of utilizing ordinary table salt as an antifog weapon. Scientists mount an airplane propeller on the floor of a big flatbed truck. The prop blows the salt 300 feet into the air, and 200 pounds of it theoretically is capable of devouring a mile-long patch of fog the width of a runway. Laboratory tests have been encouraging and experiments at an actual airport were scheduled by the Cornell University aeronautics laboratory near Buffalo, New York.

The chemicals used in the ATA tests are expensive—$4 a pound. A single big airport like O'Hare or JFK would require tons at an estimated cost of $2 million a year for total defogging. Whether special chemicals or common salt is employed, the principle is identical: fog is nothing but drops of water fused together in a kind of cloud. The chemicals merely attract water, turning the closely packed moisture into bigger raindrops.

German scientists have been experimenting with a huge vacuum cleaner which sucks the fog inside, drains the moisture and emits dry air from the other end. The Russians are working on ultrasonic vibrations that break up fog moisture into rain, although this technique has one large disadvantage: the vibrations are said to be extremely annoying to human ears. (17)

Fog dispersal is just one area in which aviation science is trying to achieve all-weather operations. Even more dramatic and positive is the progress made toward virtually automatic, "look, Ma, no hands" landings. The work dates back nearly four decades; it was on September 24, 1929, when an Army pilot became the first man to land an airplane solely by use of instruments.

He was in a single-engine military trainer. His cockpit was covered by an opaque hood which prevented any outside vision, and he flew toward a radio signal being beamed from Mitchell Field, New York. At 200 feet altitude, he lined up his plane until a special cockpit instrument hooked onto the beam. Then he followed the beam down to what he later described as a "sloppy" landing. It may have been sloppy, but it was eventful. The pilot who wrote this Braille-covered page into aviation history was Jimmy Doolittle.

Contrast that heroic but crude accomplishment with a scene that took place at Dulles International Airport on December 8, 1964.

A twin-engine United Air Lines Caravelle was making its final approach to Dulles. In the cabin sat some forty nervous reporters watching what was going on in the cockpit via two big closed-circuit television screens.

That's why these observers were nervous. Nothing was going on in the cockpit. The captain calmly poked at a couple of buttons, leaned back in his seat and took his hands off the controls and throttles. The jet dropped lower and lower toward the runway while a UAL technician supplied a play-by-play.

"We're leaving sixteen hundred feet . . . autothrottles are engaged . . . flight director is centered . . . glideslope and deviation indicators are centered . . . rate of descent five hundred feet a minute . . . throttles commanded to one hundred and thirty-four knots . . . indicated airspeed one hundred and thirty-four knots . . . horizontal and vertical ILS indicators centered . . . we're down to six hundred feet . . . down to five hundred . . ."

The throttles and yoke were moving as if manipulated by the hands of an unseen ghost.

". . . down to four hundred . . . three hundred . . . flare light on . . . flight director bars are centered . . .

throttles commanded to one hundred and ten knots . . . all indicators centered . . . radio altimeter shows fifty feet . . . ten feet . . . five feet . . . we should be on the ground."

They were. A slight, almost imperceptible bump, and the Caravelle rolled smoothly down the runway. Only now did the captain touch the throttles, pulling them back into reverse thrust. The reporters, stalwart exponents of questioning cynicism though they were, burst into spontaneous applause.

This was a perfect demonstration of AWLS—an all-weather landing system. The litany of the United "announcer" was a recitation of the technical operation of an AWLS, in this case developed jointly by Lear Siegler of California and Sud Aviation of France. The principle is virtually identical for all such systems, with only a few variations. An AWLS engages the airport's regular instrument landing system, coupling the ILS beams to the automatic pilot and throttles and literally turning the aircraft into an airborne puppet guided by invisible electronic strings.

To understand better the device and its importance, it is first necessary to understand the operation of ILS, which has been the airman's primary aid for weather landings since the late 1930s. There have been numerous refinements but basically ILS works the same as it did thirty-five years ago. It projects two radio beams to a cockpit instrument. One signal is the localizer beam, keeping the pilot on course toward his assigned runway. The second signal is the glideslope beam, which provides him with the correct angle of descent. The localizer beam appears on the ILS dial as a vertical bar; the glideslope beam is a horizontal bar. When the pilot gets both bars to form a perfectly centered cross, he knows he is heading straight for the runway and on the proper glide path.

The only drawback to ILS is that its pinpoint accuracy, so obviously essential to safety, deteriorates below 200 feet. At this altitude, pilots must take over and land visually. A handful of airports are equipped with an improved ILS that under certain conditions will permit landings with a 100-foot ceiling, but the general limit is 200 feet and visibility of a half mile.

AWLS is a means of guiding pilots safely and accurately through that final and most critical 200 feet. The Lear

Siegler system, first to receive FAA certification, is capable of steering a jet through an electronic "gate" only 46 feet wide and 26 feet high, guaranteeing touchdown within 20 feet from the runway center line and 250 feet either side of the ideal touchdown point. Other systems, such as one developed jointly by Bendix and Boeing, have demonstrated equal precision. Most have a sensor device mounted on the wings which measures the angle of attack—the gliding attitude of the plane—as it engages the ILS beams and sends signals to the throttles and controls. Another major component is an extremely accurate radio altimeter. Every system can be overridden instantly by the pilot, a feature demanded by U.S. airmen, who fear total dependence on any little "black box."

The FAA has established five present and future categories governing the conditions under which an airliner is allowed to land in bad weather.

Category I is the present rule. It permits approaches down to a ceiling of 200 feet and half-mile visibility on runways equipped with ILS. If RVR (runway visual range, which electronically measures visibility by feet) is available, the visibility can be reduced to 2,600 feet.

Category II, now in partial use, permits approaches down to an RVR reading of only 1,200 feet and a "decision height" of 100 feet, at which altitude a pilot must establish visual contact in order to make a conventional manual landing. This is the first category to require use of an approved AWLS.

Category IIIA will permit automatic landings in zero ceilings, but the RVR must indicate at least 700 feet forward visibility.

Category IIIB also will involve automatic landings, but with RVR minimums reduced to 150 feet.

Category IIIC will be a true zero-zero operation, entirely electronic, with no visual guidance even during rollout and taxiing—or, as one Pan American official put it, "Category IIIC is when you can't see the terminal building after you shut down the engines."

The airlines already are at the Category II stage and nibbling at Category IIIA. On July 7, 1967, a Pan Am 707 made a fully automatic approach and landing at London with 112 passengers aboard—the first such operation in a jetliner carrying paying passengers—using the Boeing/Bendix system. It was a proving demonstration rather than a landing under actual zero-zero conditions, for the weather was clear when Pan Am accomplished its "first."

But much experience will have to be gained under Category II before the FAA allows the airlines to enter Category IIIA and beyond. As of this writing, the industry is in a kind of Category IIA stage—a decision height of 150 feet and RVR minimums of 1,600 feet. ALPA is urging caution before proceeding to the real Category II stage, a 100-foot decision altitude and RVR minimums of 1,200 feet. The pilots' union, which believes the industry should accumulate more experience with Category IIA, claims the airlines are rushing too fast into all-weather operations.

ALPA wants a "head up" display (HUD) in every cockpit equipped with AWLS. A HUD installation would involve a kind of small, transparent screen roughly resembling a TV screen and connected to the airspeed indicator and altimeter. Readings on the latter instruments would appear on the HUD, which would be located almost at eye level; this provides the captain with vital speed and height data, plus his position relative to the runway, and at the same time allows him to look directly ahead out of his cockpit windshield. Without HUD, a pilot conceivably could have trouble watching his regular instruments during the termination phase of a Category II approach and landing—that stage at which a captain has only 100 feet of airspace left between him and the ground and about six seconds in which to decide whether a visual landing should be made or abandoned.

HUD is no theoretical designer's dream by any means. Members of an ALPA All-Weather Flying Committee have test-flown a DC-9 equipped with a head-up display system and were enthusiastic about its performance. The HUD program, however, has evoked little interest among the airlines and even less in FAA—apathy which pilots cannot understand because they think HUD could provide greater safety in ordinary landings, let alone Category II.

Whether the "rushing" charge is justified remains to be seen; ALPA has adopted a resolution "strongly recommending" that its members refuse to make landings with less than a 150-foot ceiling and 1,600 feet visibility, even when the FAA approves an airline for the full Category II stage. This could culminate in an ALPA-airline fight, for a number of carriers are operating right now under first-step Category II and virtually all are training crews for full Category II with certification applications already submitted to FAA. The airlines point out that AWLS research has been going on since 1961 with approximately 35,000 test landings made in complete safety.

The airlines were ready for Category II before the FAA was. United, American, TWA, Eastern, Delta, Western, and Pan Am alone by the end of 1967 had trained and qualified more than 6,000 pilots to make Category II landings. They also are equipping virtually their entire jet fleets with the necessary electronic gear. The other trunk lines and the local service carriers are not far behind.

FAA opened the doors to Category II in 1964, advising the industry that it would permit such operations using only specially trained crews at airports with Category II ground equipment. The latter includes improved ILS and vastly superior runway lighting. The airlines prepared their pilots faster than the FAA prepared the airports, with new runway lighting a prime bottleneck mainly because FAA revised its standards in this area. Some airports already had installed previously approved Category II lighting when the FAA decided it was not sufficiently bright and issued new standards which ran into development, testing, and manufacturing delays. As of June 15, 1969, the airlines had equipped more than 1,300 jets for Category II at a cost of $40 million, while the FAA's own program lagged.

But gradually, all the obstacles are being overcome and it is safe to predict that by the end of 1970, about 20 of the nation's major airports should be handling Category II as routinely as they have conventional ILS operations. For the airlines, virtual all-weather flying will mean even higher dependability performances and corresponding financial benefits along with increased safety.

The need for anti-weather weapons such as AWLS and fog dispersal is starkly illustrated in reciting the circumstances of just one fatal jet accident, the crash of a Canadian Pacific Airlines DC-8 at Tokyo's Haneda Airport on March 4, 1966. The flight, operating from Hong Kong to Tokyo, arrived at Haneda around 7 A.M. but was stacked up to await the lifting of heavy ground fog.

The big jet circled for an hour and the captain had just decided to try for an alternate airport when the Haneda tower informed him that visibility had improved to three fifths of a mile. This was above landing limits so the captain started his letdown, under the watchful eye of airport radar. The jet was still a mile from touchdown when the radar controller noticed that the target blip had slipped far below the proper glide path. He advised the flight to abandon the approach but even as he warned the crew, the DC-8's undercarriage snagged on the approach lights. The jetliner flipped against a concrete retaining wall at the edge of the runway, bounced over the wall onto the runway, and burst into flames.

Sixty-four persons died, including the captain, who was blamed for the accident in the Japanese government's investigative report issued two years later. The report accused him of poor judgment in attempting a landing under weather conditions that had forced other crews to continue their holding patterns or proceed to other airports.

Perhaps he *was* guilty of bad judgment; the facts, however, indicate he also might have been a victim of the booby traps so frequently implanted over those "last two miles"; possibly the tendency of altimeters to lag at low altitudes, questionable visibility reports, and the sins of omission by others that so often lead to sins of commission by pilots—in plain words, the long delays in perfecting such tools as AWLS and fog-dispersing methods despite research that started almost with the birth of the jets.

Altimeter trouble, either a malfunction or a misreading, could have been a factor in this accident and it may have played unsuspected roles in other crashes blamed on everything but the altimeter.

This instrument, in a technical sense, is nothing more than a close relative of the common aneroid barometer used in many homes. The aircraft altimeter does not really measure height; it merely measures the weight of the air, and translates that weight into terms of feet instead of pounds per square foot. Air decreases in weight as it goes higher. Thus, the altimeter gives a pilot a scale in feet corresponding to the average weight of air at a particular height.

It is a simple, usually accurate device, but it is capable of errors and it also is capable of being misread by a busy pilot. An aircraft entering a low-pressure pocket of air, for example, could have an erroneous altimeter reading ranging from a few feet to a couple of hundred feet. Some altimeters stick or lag, recording a height after the plane has left that height. Lagging is due to some malfunction, but there are other sources of altimeter error which leave behind no clues that would clear a dead pilot of blame. Airmen are convinced that many accidents attributed to navigation mistakes or plain carelessness were due to faulty or misread altimeters. The Air Force once admitted that between 1953 and 1958 there were 33 crashes involving military aircraft in which various altimeter deficiencies were either proven or suspected to be causal factors.

The newly developed radio altimeters (they project a signal toward the ground and record in terms of feet the time it takes for the signal to bounce to the plane) which are part of AWLS possess far greater low-altitude accuracy than the aneroid type, but only in a theoretical sense. They are extremely accurate over flat terrain, but their reading changes with alarming abruptness while an aircraft flies over buildings and valleys on final approach. Radio altimeters are an integral part of Category II instrumentation, but mostly as a backup to the older barometric altimeters.

A NASA altimetry expert, William O'Keefe, points out that barometric altimeters are very reliable by themselves —"riding in an elevator with a standard aircraft altimeter, you could tell what floor you're approaching just by watching the reading," he says.

The trouble, O'Keefe explains, stems from the fact that the barometric altimeter needs a static source of pressure to be measured. In an airplane, the only source is a tube or porthole located somewhere on the airframe. Adds O'Keefe:

"The big problem is getting a location that is immune to differences in things like airspeed, attitude, angle of attack, and rain; rain is particularly deadly because on final approach in rain, the static port tends to ingest water, which causes accuracy to go to hell in a hurry—at a time when you really need good altitude and rate of descent information.

"Any situation which affects the rate of airflow over the port or tube can result in static source error. Our basic aim at NASA is to develop new concepts in altitude sensing and reporting, providing basic information so accurate and dependable that air safety will improve to a marked degree."

If O'Keefe and his colleagues are successful, better altimeters will open up new flight levels for the jumbo and supersonic jets. A barometric altimeter at 65,000 to 90,000 feet would be about as trustworthy as a nymphomaniac wife. At such altitudes, one millibar of measurement on an altimeter is about a mile compared to 27 feet at sea level.

Inaccuracy is only one altimeter headache; misreading is another, and the extent of the latter may be more than anyone suspects.

Take the case of a DC-9 making a presumably routine approach to a midwest airport early in 1969. The aircraft contacted the ground nearly 5,800 feet from the runway threshold. Fortunately, the pilot maintained control, raised the gear, and staggered back to a safe altitude. There was no apparent malfunction of the altimeters and it is possible the crew simply misread them.

In 1967, a Convair 880 clipped a 90-foot-high power line *located 45 miles from the airport for which the jet was heading!* At about the same time, a jet making an approach to Kennedy was reported seen at an altitude of only 200 feet when it was *10 miles* from its assigned runway. In both cases, pilots apparently had misread their altimeters, which may seem impossible to any passenger who has not experienced the occasional difficulty of obtaining data from a rapidly unwinding instrument, while concentrating on a dozen other cockpit duties. There have been similar incidents, which will be discussed in a later chapter on the Boeing 727; for now, it is sufficient to say that the use of AWLS probably will be accompanied by adoption of some kind of altitude warning device. It would enable a pilot to pre-set the warning for an altitude below which he does not want to descend during various stages of letdown and final approach. The FAA, in fact, will require all U.S. civil jets to carry altitude alerting systems by 1971, and at least two airlines already are experimenting with test devices.

December 8, 1963.

On that date, death came to all 81 persons aboard a Pan American 707 in a disaster which, by conservative estimates, had no better than a one-in-50-million chance of ever happening.

Pan Am Flight 214 was in the final portion of a scheduled trip between San Juan, Puerto Rico, and Philadelphia, with a single stop at Baltimore. The jet left Baltimore Friendship Airport at 8:25 ——., cruising at 5,000 feet for what normally would have been not more than a twenty-minute flight. A rare winter thunderstorm was lashing the

Philadelphia area, however, and Flight 214 along with other planes wisely chose to circle at its assigned altitude until the storm passed out of the way.

A thousand feet above 214 was National 16, a DC-8, also circling cautiously while the squall line vented its fury.

The Pan Am crew advised Philadelphia Approach Control: "We're ready to go," meaning they were ready to land anytime they received permission.

"Clipper 214, stay in pattern," Approach Control advised. "I'll pull you away as soon as I can."

"Roger, no hurry," 214 replied cheerfully.

Approach Control was a hectic place on this stormy night. Several other flights on 214's frequency were demanding undivided attention. An Allegheny pilot complained he was getting kicked around by turbulence and was guided to another area. National 16 reported he couldn't hear Approach Control very well because of "snow static or something."

The controller patiently acknowledged all complaints and requests. After the squall line had passed the airport, he cleared an Allegheny flight and a small private plane for landing. National 16, still experiencing communications difficulties because of storm static, asked Approach Control to repeat a previous transmission.

"You're third in line for landing," the controller repeated.

"Okay," National 16 acknowledged.

"And how's the turbulence in your area now, National 16?" the controller inquired.

National never had a chance to answer. The next message Approach Control received was a death sentence for 81 persons.

"Mayday . . . Mayday . . . Clipper 214 out of control . . . Here we go . . ."

The stunned controller couldn't believe what he had heard.

"Clipper 214, did you call Philadelphia?" Approach Control asked.

The answer he got was not from Pan Am 214 but from the captain of National 16.

"Clipper 214 is going down in flames," he reported incredulously.

One thousand feet below him, a jagged bolt of lightning had cracked into the 707's left wing, followed by an explosion that tore off the wing. The jet began spinning toward the ground, on fire. It fell into a cornfield near Elkton, Maryland, close to the Maryland-Delaware state line, missing a house by 100 feet. One piece of wreckage dug a crater 15 feet wide and 6 feet deep in a paved road next to the cornfield.

Six thousand feet above the crash site was National 16, still circling and now receiving a lightning strike of its own.

"Ah, Philadelphia," the shaken captain paged Approach Control, "we'd like to get up to the New York area . . . we'll continue to Newark or Idlewild."

The controller said fine, but he had traffic holding at 6,000 feet between Philadelphia and New York and he'd have to try to get National 16 a higher altitude.

"We don't want to stay here," National responded tartly.

"Roger. Understand, National 16. Ah . . . turn right . . . take a one-eight-zero heading out of the New Castle area . . . this could put you into a possible smoother area."

"It's smooth enough here," was the reply. "We're just getting lightning."

National 16 banked away. Approach Control made one last effort to raise Flight 214.

"Clipper 214 . . . are you still on this frequency?"

It wasn't. Clipper 214, ironically the first production model of the Boeing 707 to come off the assembly line and thus the first U.S. jet to go into scheduled service, was the victim of a fate the experts considered virtually impossible. Not in all the years man had flown metal transports had lightning ever been an instrument of destruction. The only suspected exception was a TWA Constellation which crashed during an electrical storm at Milan, Italy, in 1959. Investigation disclosed that a static discharge, built up by the plane as it flew through the electrical storm, ignited gasoline fumes in an empty wing tank. The explosion blew off a wing.

Static discharge, however, is not the same as lightning. It is what you experience when you walk over a rug under certain temperature conditions and then touch a metal doorknob. On an aircraft, static discharge is electric energy generated by the aircraft itself as it flies through electrically charged clouds. Lightning, on the other hand, is electric energy built up outside the aircraft. Both were regarded more as annoyances than menaces. Because an airplane in flight is never grounded, and thus is a fine electricity conductor, an electrical charge merely passes through the aircraft.

The TWA accident was considered a freak, but the FAA awarded Lockheed a contract for a study of both static discharge and lightning effects on transports, as they related to possible ignition of fuel. In May of 1963, Lockheed turned in a report which said it *was* possible for lightning or static discharge to ignite fuel fumes under extremely rare circumstances. FAA scientists were still studying that report when lightning destroyed Flight 214.

Had the FAA been slow in reacting to Lockheed's findings? No fair-minded person could say this. Lockheed's own engineers had admitted that not only was a lightning-induced explosion a one-in-50-million shot, but it was not quite certain what could be done to make a rarity an impossibility. Furthermore, the chances of lightning endangering a jet seemed even more remote than with prop-driven planes. FAA statisticians reported that jets were far less likely to be hit, for several logical reasons.

As of December 1, 1963, according to FAA's figures, piston-engine planes were being struck by lightning on the average of once every 2,500 hours; propjets once every 3,800 hours; pure jets once every 10,400 hours. FAA also discovered that 75 percent of lightning strikes occurred at altitudes between 5,000 and 14,000 feet, considerably below jet airways. And jets, the FAA learned, were less prone to suffer static discharges because their outer surfaces are smoother than the fuselage and wings of older planes.

So there seemed to be no urgency in the Lockheed research report, which was more in the form of a theoretical warning than a loud alarm bell. FAA *was* considering stiffening the regulations covering lightning protection for jets before the Elkton crash, but in reality it was uncertain in which direction to move. Even long after December 8, investigators were unable to determine exactly how lightning could have knocked Clipper 214 out of the sky.

That lightning was the murderer there was no doubt. The CAB found 72 witnesses who saw lightning around the plane, 7 who actually saw a bolt strike the jet, and 27 who observed fire on the 707 seconds after seeing the lightning.

On December 13, the CAB issued a cautiously worded

statement hinting for the first time that lightning might have caused the accident.

"Investigators have found physical evidence indicating a fuel-air mixture [explosion] in the left wing fuel tanks," the CAB announcement said. "The physical evidence of the explosion is in the form of wreckage deformation in the area of the left wing fuel tank. Also Bureau of Safety investigators have found pronounced burning and pockmarking of the left wing tip, indicative of a lightning strike."

But lightning cannot ignite fuel itself. Some air must be present to vaporize the fuel first, or the fuel tank must be empty or almost empty with a residue of fuel fumes. Had Clipper 214 been afflicted with a slight fuel leak, possibly a loose rivet, which allowed fuel vapors to escape and become exposed to lightning? Another unknown factor in the deadly chain of circumstances was the outside temperature. Lockheed's research had shown that fuel vapor ignition by lightning required a certain temperature before the vapors could become combustible. Jet fuels increase in volatility as temperatures decrease.

Not for more than sixteen months did the CAB issue a report on Clipper 214's fate, and the report was an unusual admission of partial defeat. Lightning was blamed, but the CAB said "the exact mechanics of ignition" remained a mystery with further research warranted. The Board said the Boeing 707 met all FAA lightning protection requirements and that while additional protection obviously was needed, the "current state of the art does not permit an extension of test results to unqualified conclusions of all aspects of natural lightning effects."

The CAB report noted that various experiments conducted in connection with the Pan Am crash paid off in at least one area. Tests showed that direct lightning strikes on certain fuel tank access plates and caps can produce sparks inside the tank. This research led to development of a practical means of eliminating this potential danger.

But on Clipper 214, there was no physical evidence of ignition-producing sparks inside the left wing tip, even though there was plenty of strike evidence on the outside. Nor was there any sign of electric arcing inside the wing. The lightning damage nearest the fuel tank outlet on the outer left wing, where the bolt apparently penetrated, was nearly a foot from the vent edge. The vents are necessary to equalize air pressure in the fuel tanks as altitude changes.

Shortly after the Elkton tragedy, the FAA, airlines, and manufacturers agreed on additional precautionary measures. Static discharge eliminators were installed on early model 707s which lacked this device. Static discharge eliminators are tiny metal-impregnated wicks placed on the trailing edges of wings and tail stabilizers. Their main purpose is to drain off electrical discharges that accumulate when an aircraft passes through electrically charged clouds and cause interference with radio reception. They are not intended to ward off lightning, although they are a kind of miniature lightning rod. Clipper 214 was one of 97 Boeing 707s flying at the time which had wicks on the horizontal stabilizers but not on the wings.

Another step was to thicken the skin covering jet wing tips, where lightning strikes were known to occur with by far the most frequency. Access plates in the wing surface were modified to ensure adequate electrical "bonding" or contact with the wing to prevent sparking. Meanwhile, continuing research, although it failed to produce conclusive evidence that the bolt which killed Clipper 214 penetrated to fuel vapors via a vent outlet, convinced scientists this is what probably occurred.

On September 5, 1967, the FAA ordered certain models of the 707—those whose vent outlets are placed near the wing tips—equipped with one of two new safety devices. The order affected the majority of 707s and 720s. One device, designed by Fenwal, Inc., of Ashland, Massachusetts, is a flame and explosion suppression system that prevents any flame propagation through the vents. It detects a flame as it enters the fuel outlet and automatically discharges an extinguishing chemical. The alternate device ordered by FAA was an auxiliary vent tube that provides a continuous flow of air in through the regular vents and out through the auxiliary tube, thus preventing any accumulation of ignition-prone fuel vapors.

One other aftermath of Clipper 214's death is of interest to those who believe the airlines always wait for a government air safety order before acting on a major problem. TWA worked closely with Fenwal in developing a new lightning protection system, distributed the research results to all airlines—foreign as well as U.S.—and began installing the system on *all* its Boeings, at a cost of $6.5 million, before the FAA order became mandatory.

United, it may be recalled, did the same with airborne radar. American equipped its entire jet fleet with DME (distance-measuring equipment), a new safety-enhancing navigation device, months before the FAA made DME mandatory. The industry often takes an undeserved rap for apathy and lethargy in safety; in a few instances, it has been guilty of slowness or indifference, but many more times it has led rather than followed.

And sometimes, the aviation community—airline, manufacturer, and government alike—has been innocently unaware of potential hazards that existed, despite mutual devotion to safety. Even in an industry where accident prevention is a religion, not just a policy, it is unfortunately possible to make certain false assumptions and to take some things wrongly for granted—which can prove, on rare occasions, fatal, like germs hidden in a bloodstream waiting for the body resistance to lower.

This was also the story behind the misfortunes of the Lockheed Electra, the most damned and defended transport in the history of commercial aviation. And while it was not a pure jet, the lessons it taught are applicable to the future as well as the present and past.

5. THE ELECTRA STORY

Aircraft N-9705C was the fifth Electra delivered of the nine Braniff had ordered.

At 10 P.M., September 29, 1959, ten days after delivery, it sat on a ramp at Houston, Texas, a $2.4 million symphony of aluminum, steel, and foam cushioning rendered temporarily inoperative by a $300 generator that had been acting up.

It was one of those minor mechanical gremlins that occasionally plague airliners, drive dispatchers crazy, cause passengers to complain, and set pilots to muttering, "I wonder who the hell designed the goddamned part."

The balky generator had nothing to do whatsoever with what was to happen to N-9705C. Mechanics fixed it by changing the voltage regulators on both the numbers three and four engines, 28 passengers and 6 crew members boarded the plane, and N-9705C took off twenty-two minutes late as Flight 542, bound for New York International Airport with scheduled stops at Dallas and Washington, D.C.

At the very moment Flight 542 left the ground at 10:44 P.M., Lockheed Electras were busy compiling a proud and also profitable record. Nearly 100 delivered as of that date were carrying about 20,000 people daily in vibration-free comfort at speeds of more than 400 miles an hour. Passenger reaction to the roomy, well-upholstered cabins was more than favorable. Airline officials also were pleased; the Electra was the first transport in a long time that had not only met but exceeded performance and operating-economy specifications. Pilots were requesting Electra flights even when the trips were at poor hours. About the only occasional gripes heard were from those stewardesses who didn't like the Electra's galley design. It was a complaint that generally fell on deaf ears, because of a commonly held theory that no airliner galley ever built really satisfied a stewardess. It also was a commonly held theory on the part of stewardesses that (1) all galleys were designed as engineering afterthoughts and that (2) no stewardess was ever consulted until it was too late.

There had been a few operational bugs in the Electra. Excessive vibration, felt mostly in the seats in line with the four huge propellers, was the biggest problem. It was typical of the illogical difficulties which, for some unknown reason, do not appear in the thousands of hours of prototype test flights and invariably turn up only after a plane has entered the rigors of regular airline service.

Lockheed's solution was simple, although expensive. It changed the tilt of the engines, which in turn altered the angle of the prop blades. Because airliners, like automobiles, have regular warranty periods, Lockheed had to foot the $7 million bill for this comparatively minor modification.

There were a few other early troubles, chief of which involved reports of wing skin cracking—nettlesome but actually about as dangerous to structural integrity as paint chipping on an automobile fender. Some of these instances were due to the vibration mentioned before. After Lockheed corrected the vibration bug, two airlines operating Electras found further skin cracks. These were traced to harder than normal landings which transmitted the shocks from the landing gear to a small wing area.

Lockheed put reinforcing straps over the affected wing section and there were no other complaints. On September 29, 1959, the Electra seemed well on its way to achieving both airline and passenger acceptance that rivaled even the popularity of the new jets.

True, there *had* been one fatal accident involving the new turboprop. It occurred on February 3, 1959, only twelve days after American inaugurated Electra service with understandable fanfare and justifiable pride (tempered slightly by the fact that Eastern had introduced its own Electras ten days earlier).

The captain of the ill-fated flight was a fifty-nine-year-old veteran named Albert Hunt DeWitt—only one year away from retirement and one of American's senior pilots, with more than 7 million miles logged in 28,000 flight hours. On February 3 he was commanding Flight 320 from Chicago to New York's La Guardia Airport and was approaching Runway 22 in light rain and fog.

There was a subsequent welter of conflict, confusion, and controversy over what happened in the next few minutes. On one tragic fact, however, there is no dispute. Flight 320 ended in the chilling waters of the East River, nearly 5,000 feet from the threshold of Runway 22. Of the 68 passengers aboard—a full load—only 5 survived. DeWitt and a stewardess were killed. The copilot, flight engineer, and other stewardess lived through the crash which, to this day, remains a perfect example of an accident blamed on pilot error, but which also involved a number of booby traps that make an airman's own ultimate error almost inevitable.

DeWitt literally flew the Electra into the water, an unbelievable mistake for a pilot of his experience and skill. The Civil Aeronautics Board, in a report issued more than a year later, said the crew had neglected to monitor essential flight instruments—particularly those showing the plane's rate of descent and altitude. As far as his fellow American Airlines pilots were concerned, Al DeWitt and his unusually experienced copilot would have been more likely to have tried the landing blindfolded than to have ignored basic instruments during an instrument approach in bad weather.

The CAB did not agree, tagged the crew with "neglect of essential flight-instrument references," but cited a surprising number of contributing factors which in effect said 320 crashed because of mistakes made before, as well as during, the flight.

"The Board concludes there is no one factor so outstanding as to be considered as the probable cause of this accident," the CAB report said. "On the contrary, the Board has found that the accident was an accumulation of several factors or errors which, together, compromised the safety of the flight."

The "factors or errors" which the CAB listed included the crew's limited experience with a new type of airplane (of DeWitt's 28,135 hours in the air, fewer than 49 had been spent in Electras), an erroneous altimeter setting, possible misinterpretation of a new type of altimeter radically different from the kind DeWitt had used for years, the fact that American had used conventional altimeters in training its Electra crews, the lack of adequate approach lights to Runway 22, and a pilot's sensory illusion of being higher than he actually is—that frequent source of trouble for crews making poor-weather approaches over water at night.

There also was indication that DeWitt's altimeter was faulty, although the CAB said it was hardly likely that the copilot's instrument was off too. At any rate, the new altimeters were removed from all Electras and the older, more familiar models installed. Nowhere in the CAB's report was there any criticism of the Electra itself. In truth, it was the kind of accident that had happened before and did happen again, so long as airports have inadequate approach lighting. Given proper visual facilities, whatever mistakes DeWitt and his copilot made in an instrument approach probably would not have been fatal ones. They would have seen modern approach lights soon enough to tell them they were too low.

The accident had no effect on the Electra's reputation, although there undoubtedly was some early uneasiness. Only twenty-two days elapsed between the start of Eastern's Electra service and the American crash. Never in commercial aviation history had there been such a short space of time between introduction of a new airliner and its first fatal accident. But the facts of the East River tragedy, obtained relatively soon, cleared the aircraft itself.

Between American's Flight 320 and Braniff's Flight 542 eight months later lay some 80,000 hours of generally trouble-free, uneventful Electra operations. Certainly there was no indication of impending disaster when 542 pointed her nose into the clear Texas night. Her four Allison engines with their distinctive low whine bespoke effortless, almost muted power.

It will never be known whether there was any sense of prophetic doom in a remark made by Dan Hollawell, 542's First Officer. He was a veteran pilot in his own right (more than 11,000 hours) who was flying copilot that night although he held a license to command—the coveted airline transport rating that gave him the right to wear the four stripes of captain.

Hollawell was conversing idly with an Allison representative while 542's voltage regulators were being changed.

"This aircraft trims up funny," Hollawell remarked.

There was no further discussion of that curious statement. In the subsequent investigation of 542's fate, the CAB found no mention of trim difficulties or peculiarities in N-9705C's logbook or any similar complaints by pilots who had flown her before September 29.

Gracefully, effortlessly, 542 reached its assigned cruising altitude of 15,000 feet exactly sixteen minutes after takeoff. The time was 11 P.M. Second Officer Roland Longhill, the flight engineer, dutifully jotted down entries in his logbook.

Altitude 15,000. Airspeed 275 knots. Outside temperature 15 degrees. Anti-icing off.

At 11:05 P.M. the flight reported its position over Leona, Texas, as required, to San Antonio air traffic control.

"Roger 542," droned San Antonio. "Request you now monitor Fort Worth on a frequency of 120.8."

"542, roger," said Hollawell.

After switching to the new frequency, Hollawell next contacted Braniff's company radio at Dallas. The generators were working fine, he reported, but there had not been sufficient time in Houston to insulate a terminal strip on one propeller and the number three sump pump was inoperative. Both were minor items. Dallas said it figured the repair work could be done. It had no way of knowing that these two insignificant maintenance requests would be the last word heard from 542. In a sense, 542 had reported a couple of flea bites before it was to die of a monstrous metal malignancy.

Into Longhill's logbook went 542's epitaph.

"Transmission completed. 2307."

The time was 11:07 P.M.

In the next twenty-four hours a small army moved into the potato patch near Buffalo, Texas, where the plane had fallen. Its first object: the bodies of the 28 passengers and 6 crew members. The second: the wreckage in which those 34 persons had died. Every last scrap of it, from the pulverized nose found in a crater four feet deep to a few tiny pieces of aluminum, plastic, and insulating material found nearly three miles away.

One of the earliest arrivals on the scene was a burly, dark-haired man named John Cyrocki—regional accident investigator for the Civil Aeronautics Board. Like most of his colleagues, he was an ex-pilot. Like all of his colleagues, he had long ago learned the prime lessons of accident investigation. No room for sentiment. No time for horror. No excuse for personal feeling—except the unspoken sickness that fills every airman's heart at the first unbelievable sight of plane wreckage, strewn about obscenely like the half-devoured carcass of a mighty beast that had seemed unconquerable.

Every CAB (now NTSB) crash probe is carved from the same mold. Organization into teams. Each team assigned to one phase of inquiry. Each team composed of expert representatives from the groups with so much at stake in a final solution. The Air Line Pilots Association. The aircraft's manufacturer. The company that designed and made the engines. The Federal Aviation Administration, which cleared and guided the final flight and also is armed with awesome authority to order instant precautionary or corrective action based on even obscure, faint areas of suspicion. Finally, the airline itself.

Each party of interest, you might say, ready and willing to grind its own ax. ALPA to resist any verdict of pilot error. The manufacturers to clear their own products. The airline, which is the inevitable target for anger and recrimination from those who had the lives of husbands, wives, children, sweethearts, and friends snuffed out. Even the FAA to some extent, for its own rules and regulations or its standards for aircraft design may have played a role in the crash if they were in any way inadequate or obsolete.

Theoretically the CAB itself could have had something of an ax to grind. It grants the certificates under which airlines operate, and there have been two fatal accidents involving nonscheduled airlines whose fitness to fly passengers was suspect.

Yet part of the residue of every crash is the need to fix responsibility for the accident. Not for the obvious legal reasons alone, but to prevent recurrence. At the head of each team was a CAB investigator, by experience, temperament, and inbred tenacity the theoretical personification of objectivity.

In a sense, he drew on the subjective zeal of the conflicting parties. He united them in a common cause, knowing that they would seek the truth as he did, up to the point where their partiality could color interpretation of the truth. And such interpretation was the job of the CAB and no one else. The teams gather the evidence, unearth the clues, and produce the facts. Once this is accomplished, however, their role changes from active to passive and, like detectives who have suddenly become suspects, they must await the verdict of an agency that has no ax to grind.

This was the philosophy behind the investigation of Braniff Flight 542, as it was in the approximately 150 U.S. fatal airliner crashes that preceded it and as it will be in the accidents that follow it. Not all the verdicts were fair, just, and accurate. But the batting average for truth has been as high as anyone can expect, considering the ever-present margin for interpretive error, the human limitations of those involved, the frequent lack of solid evidence, and the absence of testimony from the only men who really know what happened in a fatal crash—the flight-deck crew.

Philosophical, however, was not the word for John Cyrocki's frame of mind as he organized the usual investigative teams—witness interrogation, structures, operations, systems, and engines. He had not been on the scene for more than a few minutes when he got the chilling news. The left wing and its engines had been found a mile and a half from the potato patch where the bulk of the fuselage wreckage lay. And remnants of the right wing were spread along the flight path leading to the farm.

Midair disintegration? Sabotage? Structural failure from some unknown cause? The latter is an instant suspect in any catastrophic inflight breakup of an airframe. But to Cyrocki and everyone else, the very possibility of structural failure was catastrophic in itself. This was a brand-new airliner, the proud product of every aeronautical test known to modern science, the legacy of all the research and progress that engineers had accomplished since the first metal transport was built more than three decades before.

The weather on September 30 was hot and sticky. The proprietor of the local feed store came out and sprayed the scene with a makeshift disinfectant, a conglomeration of insecticide and embalming fluid. A battalion of 300 soldiers from nearby Fort Hood arrived to aid in the search for wreckage. Cyrocki spread them out in a skirmish line for a half mile wide and sent them through the chigger-infested woods bordering the White farm.

"Don't pick up any wreckage," he warned. "Just mark its location and keep going until you've found every scrap."

Most of what they found was in pieces not much bigger than a soup bowl. Approximately 90 percent of the forward fuselage, for example, was in crushed sections of two square feet or less. Two hundred feet away was the center section, fragments of the right wing, and what was left of the rear-cabin structure.

The cockpit was virtually unrecognizable. But searchers did find the flight engineer's log sheet. At 2300 (11 P.M.), he had recorded an indicated air speed of 275 knots—314 miles per hour, and with a tail wind, the plane probably was nudging 400 MPH.

At this point, the CAB knew only how fast 542 was going and how high it was just seven minutes before the unknown struck. It knew—again from the crumpled but still readable log—that engine and airfoil anti-icing systems were off and the outside temperature was 15 degrees above zero. Weather at the time of the accident was good, with partly cloudy skies. A check with pilots flying in the area before and after the crash turned up no reports of lightning, turbulence, or precipitation.

The witnesses team went to work contacting every known person who either heard 542 or saw it. The results were intriguing but also mystifying.

An engineer who had had some experience working jet power plants was driving home in his car when he saw a light flash in the sky. Like a phosphorous fireball, he recalled—first glowing, then subsiding, next flaring up, and finally fading. But after the light, he heard a noise that he described as deafening. He could compare it only to the sound of a jet breaking the sound barrier.

Other witnesses told of the noise in descriptions that agreed on only one point: it was loud.

"The clapping of two boards together," said one.

"The sound of thunder," was another.

"The roar of a jet breaking the sound barrier."

"A whooshing, screaming noise."

"A creaking noise like a big bulldozer."

"Just an awful explosion."

Among numerous witnesses, the investigators found agreement on a curious phenomenon.

"When the sound came," said one farmer, "every coon dog for miles around started howling."

Interrogation revealed the truth of that observation. Every nearby farmer owning a hound reported that the animal began howling shortly after 11 P.M. It was a clue, although its significance was not clear.

The CAB went out and recorded twelve known noises of unusual intensity. Jet aircraft. Sonic booms. Propellers whirling at supersonic speeds. Electras in normal flight. Electras diving and climbing. Also intentionally random noises having not the remotest connection with an airplane or any part of one.

Cyrocki gathered the best of the witnesses and played the tapes for them individually. None was told the source of the noises. Each was asked to pick out the sound most like the one heard shortly after 11 P.M. on September 29. The witnesses picked two noises from the tape as coming the closest. One was that of a prop at supersonic speed. The other was the sound of a jet aircraft.

The structures team, meanwhile, was having its own troubles. There is no phase of accident investigation work that is more difficult, and some veterans of crash inquiries sadly commented they had never seen an aircraft in so many small pieces.

Actually, most totally fatal crashes look the same even to experts until they delve into the wreckage—a scattered pile of meaningless, twisted, scarred, and scorched junk, heartbreaking in its awful finality and unbelievable to airmen, who take so much pride in their magnificent creations of metal and power.

The Braniff wreckage scene contained something even the veterans had never seen before at a crash—blood. There were obvious traces of blood all over the sweet potato patch where most of the wreckage lay. Some news reports mentioned this item as delicately as possible, and to anyone fearful of flying it must have made a bad crash seem even worse. When the CAB got around to looking at flight 542's cargo manifest, however, it discovered a simple explanation. The plane was carrying a shipment of whole blood to a Dallas hospital. The containers had ruptured on impact.

Wreckage distribution was important, for it would show the pattern of what must have been midair disintegration. Air Force helicopters helped pinpoint locations. Bulldozers gouged out paths through the woods so the troops from Fort Hood could advance their search line. An Air Force photo reconnaissance plane was flown in from Langley Field, Virginia, to make overall shots of the entire crash scene. This latter chore had to be done when a cloud cover disappeared, so the plane could fly high enough not only to take in the whole area, but to keep farmers from filing phony claims for "lost" livestock allegedly frightened by the noise (one of the minor hazards of air accident probes).

Some 'copters sweeping at treetop level over an area some distance from the nose crater found some puzzling pieces of aluminum foil. These, however, quickly were identified as chaff used in an Air Force radar training exercise. The foil, a World War II innovation, is designed to interfere with radar tracking of aircraft, but there was no possible connection with this accident.

Gradually the ground and air search parties located the severed jigsaw puzzle that had been a proud airliner. The wreckage at the nose crater consisted of the cockpit, some forward fuselage structure, and a few seats. Back in the direction from which Flight 542 had come was the center cabin structure 225 feet away.

Two hundred and thirty feet away were the tail cone, vertical fin and rudder, and the inboard stabilizers.

Seventeen hundred and sixty feet away was the right stabilizer.

Four thousand and eighty feet away was the left stabilizer.

Fifty-three hundred feet away was the nacelle covering of the number four engine, known as QEC (for quick engine change).

Eighty-six hundred and forty feet away was the left wing, including the number four engine and number two QEC and propeller.

Ninety-nine hundred feet away was the number one propeller and gear box.

A full 13,900 feet away (2.3 nautical miles) was the last item located—a 9-inch section of hydraulic line that had been inside the number two fuel tank.

The engines on every plane are numbered from left to right. On a four-engine airliner, that means numbers one and two are on the left wing, three and four on the right. The various components of numbers one and two engines, plus sections of the left wing itself, were found the greatest distance from the nose crater. The entire wreckage pattern, allowing for the wind displacing some of the lighter pieces, was in a fairly straight line starting from about 17 miles from the Leona VOR (the last radio check point) to the White farm. The first piece of the puzzle had slipped into place, just a tiny corner of a picture called Flight 542.

Structural failure of the left wing, then general disintegration.

This was not any complete answer, of course. There was the voluminous testimony from witnesses who had seen an apparent explosion, variously described as resembling a huge camera flashbulb or an electric welding arc, followed by a reddish-orange fireball. Did the wing fail because of an explosion or prolonged fire, or did the flash of fire result from igniting of fuel as it spewed from the ruptured wing?

The wreckage was taken to Dallas warehouse, where the Structures Group began a mockup, or reconstruction. The work went on steadily for twenty-six days—from October 12 to November 6. The reconstruction then was interrupted by a spate of aircraft accidents elsewhere that took several CAB experts away from Dallas, much to the concern and annoyance of Braniff pilots working on the case. They did not blame the CAB, for to the ALPA participants it was another example of the Board's woefully understaffed Bureau of Safety at the time being forced to spread itself too thin. (An aftermath of this and other crashes was a long-needed Congressional appropriation that allowed the Bureau to increase its investigators from 60 to 100.)

On November 23 Structures resumed the weary task of dipping into the two huge barrels jammed with tiny metal fragments and trying to fit them into larger pieces of wreckage.

The mockups of N-9705C, constructed under the supervision of CAB Structures expert John Leak, were aimed mainly at determining whether fire preceded or followed the wing severance. As usual, it consisted of wood-and-chickenwire frames on which fragments were placed in their correct relative positions. Contrary to popular belief, seldom is a mockup assembled as a complete airplane, and those who see one are disappointed. They expect to view a reassembled aircraft that looks almost capable of flying again.

"Instead," Leak himself once commented, "what they see resembles an organized garbage collection."

But as in the past, this particular garbage collection yielded some valuable information in the sense that it eliminated possible suspects, even though it did not furnish the identity of the guilty party. The mockups were done in sections—one involving the fuselage, another the engine structure, a third the wings and so on.

One of the theories being kicked around was a possible fire in the starter compressor, housed in the lower-rear fairing of the inboard engine nacelle. The compressor is driven hydraulically and has a magnesium case. When investigators pulled up the louvered cover panel, they found heavy soot streaks from the louvers that were typical of in-flight fire.

But during the mockup, Leak fitted in the adjacent cover panel, which had not been subjected to any heat or fire. Engineers studied this area on an undamaged Electra and determined that any smoke exiting through the louvers had to flow over the interior of this adjacent panel. Leak concluded that the intense ground fire enveloping the magnesium case had forced smoke through the louvers at such high velocity that the smoke traces appeared similar to in-flight fire.

Leak also discovered that skin-panel fragments, when hung on the mockup frame, were not burned in any reasonable pattern. One piece would be heavily sooted. The adjacent part would be completely clean.

The left rear side of the fuselage was covered with a fair amount of soot which was in both straight rearward and spiral patterns. No particular clue here, but the possibility of in-flight fire *prior* to breakup was raised again when laboratory tests on the rear windows showed they had been subjected to prolonged burning at intense temperatures.

The heat had been sufficient to "craze" the Plexiglas and indicated longer exposure to flames than would have come from a flash fire produced by a wing fracture. But additional mockup work explained this puzzler. It revealed that when the wing severed, the wing-to-fuselage fillet was exposed in the shape of a scoop—a freak distortion of metal that could hold and gradually feed out about 40 gallons of kerosene. This had prolonged the invasion of fire on the rear fuselage.

In desperation, Leak and Cyrocki went back to the unlikely possibility of a tire blowout or even a hot wheel brake. Either might have ignited fuel or hydraulic fluid from broken lines in the wheel well. But the probers found the wheel-well door-actuating rods that had been thrown free of the ground fire area. They were as unmarked and clean as the day they came out of the factory.

By now it was definite that the fire had occurred after the wing broke off. The fracture itself was close to the fuselage and displayed evidence of strong twisting and yanking forces. But there was absolutely no sign of metal fatigue, no trace of any inherent structural weakness.

Sabotage was an early suspect but was discounted as soon as the fire damage was shown to have followed the breakup.

Could 542 have maneuvered violently to escape a collision? The FAA could not locate a single aircraft that had been anywhere near the Electra.

Could it have been trying to avoid a missile or could a missile have hit the left wing? Missile bases as far away as the eastern seaboard were checked. Nothing had been fired.

The CAB tracked down other possible but futile clues. An Eastern Electra had suffered some minor wing damage when excessive fuel tank pressure caused an overflow during fueling. Damage from such a source may appear farfetched, but an Electra's tanks can be gorged with 5,500 gallons of kerosene in twenty minutes. Yet inspection of N-9705C's maintenance history disclosed no similar incident. Another Electra had experienced a small electrical fire near the wing roots, but there was not a shred of evidence that 542 had encountered anything like this. A third Electra had suffered a tire blowout in the air, causing damage to an engine nacelle. But nobody had ever heard of an exploding tire causing a wing to come off.

There was a great deal of speculation on the remark First Officer Hollawell had made just before the last takeoff from Houston—"This aircraft trims up funny." This suggested some kind of stabilizer or autopilot difficulty. But it also could have been the result of a slightly unbalanced fuel load, uncommon but not unknown. At any rate, the CAB never could trace the reason for Hollawell's comment, nor could it find any indication of trim complaint on the logbook. Besides, no two pilots trim an airplane in exactly the same way. What may seem like unsatisfactory trim to one may be perfectly acceptable to another.

At a fairly early stage of the investigation there was a widespread belief that the number two engine had caught fire, that the blaze could not be quenched, and that the flames eventually weakened the wing to such an extent that it failed. But this was belied by the Electra's superb fire-control system, one of the best ever designed. And again, the inspection of fire damage later knocked down this theory entirely, just as it knocked down any suspicion of sabotage. Furthermore, no engine fire in the history of commercial aviation ever had destroyed a plane in less than sixty seconds. There had been absolutely no emergency message from Flight 542. Fire would have been one item of serious trouble affording sufficient time for the crew to advise something was wrong.

How about the various noises witnesses had reported? Some had likened what they had heard to propellers whirling at supersonic speeds. This suggested the possibility of a runaway engine—and there had been solid evidence that the crew had feathered numbers three and four props. But these are on the right wing. It was the left wing that failed first. Besides, flight tests demonstrated beyond any doubt that an overspeeding engine caused no control difficulties with an Electra.

Some Lockheed engineers had a theory that a runaway prop going into supersonic speed without warning would have startled the crew to such an extent that the pilot flying the plane instinctively had reduced power and then yanked back on the controls to bring the nose up and reduce airspeed so abruptly that the wing failed. After all, this was an airplane relatively new to the crew, none of whom had any idea what a runaway prop engine combination might sound like.

The theory didn't fit this particular crew, however. The captain of Flight 542, Wilson Elza Stone, was a forty-seven-year-old veteran of more than 20,000 logged flight hours. He had earned a long and enviable reputation of being positive yet smooth, demanding yet gentle, with every airplane he ever flew. The check pilot who rated Stone when he was transitioning to Electras remarked later that "he flew the Electra like he had written the operations manual himself."

For that matter, Lockheed itself admittedly was grasping at straws. It was too difficult to imagine how even a sharp pull-up at high speed could have torn a wing off.

This raised another question: could the plane somehow have plunged into a sudden, high-speed dive that resulted in the wing's separating when Stone tried to bring it out?

Lurking in every investigator's mind, like a nagging, uneasy conscience, was the phrase uttered by one farmer and backed up by so many of his neighbors: "Every coon dog for miles around started howling."

What kind of a sound frequency could have disturbed dogs in that way? Some engineers pointed out that in a dive surpassing 400 miles an hour an Electra's props would be whirling at supersonic speeds. One witness listening to those tape recordings had likened the sound to that of a supersonic prop.

But assuming the Electra had gone into an inadvertent dive, this would have involved some kind of control problem, and there was no evidence of any control malfunction. The elevator and aileron booster mechanisms were tested and found normal. The autopilot was too badly crushed for any tests, but even if this had engaged without warning and locked the controls in a dive position, it could have been disengaged immediately. Also the breakup, from a trajectory study of the wreckage distribution, indicated that structural failure began at the cruising altitude of 15,000 feet. (Further trajectory tests showed that failure also could have occurred at 5,000 feet and resulted in the same wreckage pattern, but the lower altitude did not jibe with witness estimates of the fireball height.)

Three months after the crash, the CAB was unable to come up with the slightest inkling of a probable cause. On January 12, 1960, investigator-in-charge Cyrocki called a meeting of his investigative teams. He also invited representatives from the National Aeronautics and Space Administration, American, Eastern, the Army's Bureau of Aircraft Accident Research, and personnel from the Federal Aviation Agency's Los Angeles engineering division who, as employees of the CAA, the FAA's predecessor agency, had certificated the Electra. The meeting lasted five days, and one participant commented that "it looked like a re-evaluation of the whole Electra certification program."